REVELATION OF THE SECRET OF BIRDS AND FLOWERS

BY

The Learned Sheikh Izzidin son of
Abdusalam son of Ahmad son of Ghanim,
Al-Muqaddisi (Of the Sacred Place):
Upon him the Mercy of Almighty God!

THE OCTAGON PRESS
LONDON

THE BOOK OF THE
REVELATION OF THE SECRETS
OF THE BIRDS AND FLOWERS

by
The Learned Sheikh Izzidin Al-Muqaddisi (d. 1280)
from four Arabic manuscripts edited by
J H Garcin de Tassy, 1821

translated by
Irene Hoare and Darya Galy, 1979

translation edited by Denise Winn, 1980

English and Arabic verification by
Al-Arif Dr A Halim Abbassi, D Litt, and M Y A Shadhili

with a Preface by
Al-Hajj Anwar K Winstone-Hamilton, 1980

original Dedication to
Baron Silvestre de Sacy, by J H Garcin de Tassy

Copyright © 1980 by Octagon Press Ltd.

Published for the Sufi Trust by The Octagon Press Ltd.

ISBN 900860 75 8

First published 1980
Reprinted 1987

Printed & bound in Great Britain by
Redwood Burn Limited, Trowbridge, Wiltshire

CONTENTS

PREFACE

Readers accustomed to thinking of Sufism, or Islamic mysticism, in terms of denominationalism may be surprised to note that in this book reference is approvingly made to such apparently unconnected traditions as those of Abraham, Noah, the Israelites, Jesus and King Solomon, as well as to the Koran, Mohammed and Ishmael. Those who have read widely in Sufi literature, however, will note that it is only with the deterioration of spiritual understanding of the past few centuries that sectarianism has seemed to be found among those regarded as Sufis.

According to such authorities as Bayazid Bistami, one of the greatest Masters (died 875 of the Christian Era), there has been a succession of expressions of what we now call Sufism, each appropriate to its epoch, allegorised in these words:

"Its seeds were set at the time of Adam, they sprouted under Noah and flowered under Abraham. Grapes formed at the time of Moses, and they ripened at the time of Jesus. In the time of Mohammed, they were made into pure wine."

This book also partakes somewhat of the activity of supersession of presentation alluded to by Bayazid, for it has an interesting history and context.

Many readers in the West as well as in the East know of Fariduddin Attar (The Chemist) and especially his book, *The Conference of the Birds. The Secrets of the Birds and Flowers*,* coming about a century after Attar's writing, resembles it in certain interesting ways, and may be said to belong to the same genre: representing the culmination of a series of Sufi teaching-books, each designed for a later audience, in accordance with the characteristic 'updating' which is so marked in Sufi teaching, as distinct from the scholastic tendency to regard texts as sacrosanct. *The Secrets of the Birds and Flowers*, reputedly the finalisation of the corpus of material which had been given out from far earlier times, appeared in Syria at about the same time that the *Roman de la Rose* was to be found in France.

*Sometimes called *The Secrets of the Birds, Flowers and Animals*.

"In fact," as de Tassy notes†, speaking of the French romance, "this romance is generally and rightly regarded as mystical, and the mysterious rose that man has to conquer is God himself."

Muqaddisi's work is partially derived from an earlier Sufic composition, *The Awakening of the Sleeper*, and also resembles a book known as *The Gift of the Brethren of Purity*. Further East, its connection with the Urdu mystical *Rose of Bakawali* has also been noted. Most European readers versed in this subject will recognise the rose motif as being very much in evidence following the date of the *Roman* in the West, infusing the mysticism of the church, of special bodies like the alchemists, and of other mystics detached from any formal confessional format. As recently as the mid-seventeenth century, we find, in Europe, *La Vertue ensigné par les Oiseaux* (R. P. Alard le Roy, Liège 1653) and other writings noted by de Tassy.

The importance of the present version of the *Birds and Flowers*, however, is due to the conviction among its students, in the seven hundred years since its author died, that this form constitutes the final expression of the materials contained in the tradition.

The Learned Sheikh Izzidin b. Abdusalam b. Ahmad b. Ghanim, Al-Muqaddisi also wrote other allegories. It is often said, however, that these have not survived—or are not now employed in Sufi teaching—because their application was valid only for a limited space of time. The present edition is derived from four different manuscripts consulted by M. Garcin de Tassy, and published in Paris, in Arabic and French, by the Imperial Press in 1821. In addition to containing many Sufi technical terms and phrases ('die before your death', 'wine', 'sensuality', 'man asleep' and so on) it also shows us how certain varieties of Sufi literature were projected in such a way as both to accord with orthodox religion of the Islamic persuasion and also to maintain concepts which are rarely emphasised in formalistic religion.

The experiential approach, which insists upon inner development and progress as distinct from the piety of appearances; the employment of love-poetry; the bewitchingly

†*Language of the Birds*, Paris, 1864, Introduction by Garcin de Tassy.

effective Arabic of the original; the varietal nature of man and of communities—these are all here given a many-sided and often surprisingly 'modern' flavour.

Especially interesting is the way in which various human characteristics are noted and then seen to be over-developed so as to become vices in many cases. Again, one is constantly surprised by the flexibility of approach, and the psycho-spiritual perception by which Muqaddisi notes the shifting emotions of individuals and classes of people; the strengths and weaknesses of different postures of ideological emphasis; the balance between devotion and emotion. It has been said, perhaps with truth, that there is no document of such age to touch this one for a combination of mystical insight and understanding of human psychology.

1980   K. Winstone-Hamilton

INTRODUCTION

by Izzidin Al-Muqaddisi

In the name of God the merciful, the compassionate.

Praise be to God whose remoteness is nearness, whose nearness in remoteness, whose greatness defies any manner of description; whose sanctity so sublime is inestimable, limitless. Praise be to God who brought the World forth from non-existence; who infused in each creature glimpses of wisdom which surely affirm the existence of a creator; and who has endowed man with reason for judging between opposites. It is through the inspiration of this almighty God that man has acquired the knowledge that is his and may distinguish true from false, reality from error.

Anyone who gives himself to serious thought, and is guided and sustained by honest and pure intentions, may come to understand that all creatures are in the hands of Providence; and that Providence, just as it condemns some to misfortune, brings happiness to others and heaps them with favours and precious gifts. Nothing can stem the mercy of God: nor can anything give that which He himself withholds.

If your mind's eye were not diverted by extraneous interests, if nothing were polluting the mirror of your awareness and if you listened with the ear of attention, each creature could tell you of its unfulfilled desires and the pain it has suffered from this privation.

Listen to the zephyr in the foliage, murmuring at the tears of the clouds that ebb and flow like the movements of the sea, wailing at the gentle smile of lightning after the roar of thunder's laughter.

Then think of spring: it comes to bring you joy with its happy hail of roses; it comes to tell you that the bitter cold has passed. The dark winter retreats as it approaches you with a multi-coloured mantle, to clothe the naked fields. The Egyptian willow weeps to you its woes in the movement of its boughs; the marguerite disarms you with a host of varied flowers, waving before you banners tinged with their happiness. The narcissus rises on its stem as if for prayer. The anemone appears in her tattered dress, striking her rose-like cheeks as if in grief for the loss of one dear to her. The pomegranate is telling you how much he suffers from the over-ardent fire kindled within him by the cruelty and scorn of his departed friend. The nightingale on the swinging bough modulates its soft notes, as if gently stroking the strings of a lyre.

The lover, a prey to love's melancholy, is no longer the master of his own passion and confides to the zephyr the adored name which he had so carefully kept concealed: stirred by the fragrance of Najd, home of his mistress, he wanders drunk with pleasure in solitary places, sanctuaries of their secret trysts, seeking refuge at the side of this divine beauty who knows the love that he speaks and the love that he hides in his heart.

The mystic, filled with gratitude for all the favours which he has received, prepares to dig deeper into the mine of wisdom; from milk he wishes to take only the purest cream and he knows that no being has been created by God simply to be left, alone and useless. For every creature occupies the place assigned for it, never straying from the road marked for it and each is a testimony to the truth of God's promises and warnings. There is nothing, nothing, which does not pay tribute of praise to the Most High. To this unanimous concert of beings I join my own small voice and I pray Almighty God to help my efforts and inspire me with genius.

I bless and salute His Prophet to whom he vouchsafed a revelation to blaze out His glory and whom he guided across the celestial spheres during the famed Night-Journey. May God's mercy and favour rest forever on this messenger, his companions and his descendants!

Full of these thoughts, I looked on the universe with eyes undistracted and, lighted by the torch of divine help and discernment, I saw that all beings speak the existence of the Creator and that those who cannot express themselves through speech adopt silent language as a form for their feelings. So I opened myself to the hints that glimmer in the things of nature and fathomed the allegories that they represent. I realised that everything is, in reality, gifted with the capacity to communicate, either through the senses or by means of the intellect; more than that, I came to realise that the language of silence is more eloquent than speech, more true to essence than words can ever be.

When someone has spoken, one can concur with the correctness of his observations or else refute his words; whereas the language of emblems is the language of certainty and truth. But then, he who uses the figurative mode speaks only to those who have higher perceptions: while he who expresses himself through conventional means communicates with the ordinary state, common to us all.

I have written this work to explain the different allegories communicated to me in my meditations by animals and plants and even inorganic things; I can tell, too, what the solitary blackbird told of his listless repose, and his restless careening through the fields. May alert and perceptive people find useful lessons in these writings; for people of depth and reflective nature, may they act as a reminder of their duties; and may they convey to everyone salutary instruction. Whoever enters the spirit of my interpretations and understands my parables will derive pleasure from my book; whoever finds them alien will gain nothing.

I do not know what thought urged me to go one day and contemplate what was brought forth by the hands of the eternal God; that which was created by divine Wisdom, which always has purpose and always achieves its aim.

With this end in mind I went into a large garden. Soft lawns ruffled by the zephyr's quivering breath were its carpet; sweet aromas emanated from the flowers; the leafy heights of the trees murmured and stirred, the boughs swinging to the breath of a spring wind. The nightingale warbled softly, sighing with its tunes, lisping of its loves.

Here a stream ran across a meadow, there a waterfall cascaded wantonly; further on, fresh brilliant flowers studded the velvet lawn; in every direction vivid and varied landscapes met my eye. At the sight of it all I asked myself: can there be a more delightful place, a more pleasing solitude? Ah, would that I had a dear and true-hearted friend with whom I could commune deeply!

I thought, suddenly, that I might catch these words in the silent and enigmatic language of nature.

Can you find a better friend than I? Can you hope to hear more eloquent answers than mine? There is nothing in all that you see that does not express itself in the language of symbol, nothing whose approaching end is not signalled by its state, manifested in its mode of being. Apply yourself, therefore, to understanding this language, if you are capable of hearing it.

VERSES

See the morning zephyr whose breath exhales fragrant currents that ripple through the air. Sometimes it makes sad, and plaintive sounds: like a lover bereft of his loved one; sometimes, like one reunited with a beloved mistress, it is imbued with exquisite perfumes. The clouds which let fall their refreshing showers, the lulling coo of the dove, the quiver of the branch that supports it, the half-light of the morning dawn, the lime tree when lightning and thunder-charged clouds come to shake its flowers, the spring which, accompanied by its herald, the rose, brings to nature such charming changes—all that exists (and which is destined for your use, O man, unconscious of God's favours), everything, yes everything, praises God's bounty, acknowledges His existence, thanks Him, blesses Him. Yes, from each and every thing, one can extract a proof of His unity.

ALLEGORY I
The Zephyr

My attention was first awakened by the wailing of the zephyr which, wanting to extol the language and the luxury of its breath, seemed to shape this soliloquy from its enigmatic sighs:

I, the faithful messenger of lovers, carry on my wings to loved ones, who alone can heal pain, the burning sighs of those sick with love for them. I am a faultless deliverer of the secrets entrusted to me and I speak my message exactly as it was spoken. If I meet a traveller, my breath becomes softer; it is just cajolery and friendly jesting. I act towards him as *he* acts, however: if he is good, I caress him with a luxurious breeze; but if he is wicked, then I molest him with my troublesome blowing.

My light fragrant breath brings health to the sick and makes peaceful and pleasant the midday rest. If my rustling sways the leaves, the lover cannot restrain his sighs; and if he hears my murmur he will confide his suffering to his mistress's ear. Gentleness and softness form my essence: only he who receives God's favours knows how to appreciate me.

Is not the purity of the air the product of my life-giving breath? And do not imagine that the changefulness you observe in my nature is caused by a trifling whim; it is for your use and benefit that my breath follows the seasons through their various changes.

In the spring, I blow from the North, I fertilise the trees and make night equal with day.

In summer my breath, coming from the East, quickens the growth of flowers and gives to the trees their most perfect aspect of beauty.

In autumn I blow from the South; it is then that all fruit reaches perfection and enters the last stage of its maturity.

Last of all, in the winter I blow from the West; and now I relieve the trees of the burden of their fruit and I dry the leaves without hurt to the branches. It is I who ripen fruit, give to the flowers their brilliant colours, endow the streams with silvered chains; I who cause the pollen to reach and fertilise the trees and I make the sighs of the inflamed heart reach the inflamer; it is my fragrant breath, too, that tells love's pilgrim when he is drawing near to the tents of his beloved.

VERSES

It pleased the breeze to spread its fragrance and to intoxicate me with this delicious perfume. When the first sighs of this love which consumes me escaped from my breast, the zephyr seemed to echo them with his dying breath. The fresh scented morning breeze should have quenched the thirst of my passion; but during the night it had passed close to those familiar spring pavilions and lofty mounds, becoming suffused with the aroma flowing from my mistress's tent; and it heightened the fierceness of my love's fire and suffering.

Intoxicated with pleasure, I could not come to my senses nor could I collect my thoughts. Mindful of the zephyr's voice, I understood the secret which my rivals could not guess and I heard what they did not hear. I learned that, in a place where 'wine' arouses sensuality of the purest form, my adored friend has allowed her glorious beauty to be seen without any veil to conceal her charms and has shown to her faithful lovers that ravishing face, ordinarily shielded from even the most avid glances.

ALLEGORY II
The Rose

Encouraged by understanding what the zephyr seemed to utter, I was trying to interpret the blackbird's whistle and wondering at the flowers' heady hues when the rose, in an exhalation of perfume, gently announced its approach: and in its silent language intimated this:

I am the guest who comes to call between winter and summer, my visit as short as the apparition of the night-wraith; make haste to enjoy the time that I am in flower and remember that time is a sharp sword. I wear both the colour of the mistress and the garb of the mystic who is a lover; I cover in perfume those who inhale my breath, I foster an unexpected emotion in the young beauty who receives me from the hand of her friend. I am to man just a passing visitor; and whoever hopes to hold me fast hopes in vain.

Why do I suffer the harshness of fate which brings me only bitterness, so that whenever I open a bud thorns encircle me and press me from all sides? These prickly stings and sharp arrows wound me, shedding my blood on my petals, to stain them vermilion. This is what I endure; and yet I am the most noble of guests, the most elegant of travellers. But alas! None is at shelter from torment and pain; at least he who is able to bear them will attain the object of his desires.

Resplendent in my freshness and clothed in the robe of beauty, suddenly I am plucked by the hand of the Nazarines and taken from amidst the flowers to the imprisonment of a vase: then my body turns to water and my heart is burned; my flesh is torn and my strength is sapped; my tears fall, yet no one stops them, no one feels pity. My body falls prey to the ardour of fire, my tears themselves drown, my heart is distressed. The moisture I make is a token of the torments I endure by fire. Those consumed by a burning heat receive from my essence a lightening of their pain and those troubled by desire are grateful to breathe my musk-like scent. When my outward charms withdraw from man, my inner quality still remains amongst them. The people of Knowledge, skilled at drawing such learning from my transient beauty, await the time when my flower adorns the gardens; while lovers yearn that this time could last for evermore.

VERSES

Although I left you bodily, is not my spirit always close to you! Think of it and you will see that my presence and my absence are the same. How right was he who said to me: one can compare you to the rose that fades but leaves behind its essence!

ALLEGORY III
The Myrtle

No sooner had the myrtle sensed the speech of the rose than in the same language it spoke to it these words:

Already the clouds seem, as if playing at backgammon, to be scattering brilliant pearls; the zephyr tells its secret; the yellow *behar* is spreading its scented treasures; spring is proud of the garlands that garnish it; flowers, wanting only to please, are not content in embellishing the most beautiful gardens and still yearn to shine elsewhere; the nightingale sings of his loves; the grove, meeting-place of the lover, takes on its spring-time brilliance once again. Come, O my companion, let us enjoy ourselves and, proud of our beauty, let us grasp at the elusive instants of joy, so that not even the shortest moment can pass us by!

The rose, surprised by the myrtle's proclamation, spoke again at once, and in these words: How can you hold forth in this way, you, the prince of fragrant plants! Even if I anger you, you should not express yourself so; your pernicious advice makes you unworthy of the distinguished rank you occupy among flowers! If *you* are to stray, who will be able to reach the goal? Who will lead, if *you* lose the way? You enlist your subjects to come and play by your side, you encourage them to make merry. What! To be at the head of others and to have such unwholesome intent! Do not let your beauty intoxicate you, just because your stems sway gently, your leaves are a harmonious green and your line is a noble one. You are the image of youth's happy days that flee so fast, only to vanish. Such are the moments, always too short, that are spent with an adored beloved; such, also, are those fantastic illusions which come to assail the imagination at night, too brief to be broken and yet, in duration, endless.

Already, at the coming of spring, fields cover themselves with a cloak of green spangled with a thousand flowers, their forms as various as those of the animals that live upon the earth. Of these flowers, some come to delight the sense of smell and then they fade; others serve as happy symbols and whole lines can be lifted from the language that they speak; these are the playthings of the harshness of fate; those others, cut off from all life, are spread over hillocks in the countryside.

Amongst vegetables there are some whose fruits are eaten and which serve as a basic food for men; but very few escape the devouring flames. Yet, if there were no fate, they would all be spared the cruelty of this end.

Brother, do not let yourself be seduced by the semblance of pleasures offered you by the caravanserai of this world; the gaping jaws of the lions of death are ready to receive you. Such is the advice I feel beholden to give you. Farewell.

ALLEGORY IV
The Narcissus

The narcissus contemplated his companion, the myrtle, and then explained his own thoughts in this way:

Being, as I am, always close to other flowers, it is ever my wish to treat them with care. I talk with them by moonlight and constantly I am their companion; my beauty sets me at the head of my friends but nevertheless I am also their servant; therefore, should any wish to learn, I am well equipped to teach the obligations which service must entail.

I draw around myself the belt of obedience and, ever ready to carry out commands, I hold myself as humbly as a slave. When other flowers bend their heads, I do not bend mine with them; nor do I raise my head towards those who share my food; I am never sparing with my scent for those who want to breathe it; I never forget what I owe to those who make use of me and I never rebel against the hand that plucks me. At all times I quench my thirst from my cup which is, for me, like a robe made rich by the purity of its design; an emerald stem acts as my foundation and gold and silver go to make my dress.

When I reflect upon my imperfections, I can only lower my eyes to the ground, in confusion; and when I meditate upon my future, I think forward to the moment that fate has set for the end of my existence. It may seem strange that I should give myself over to such dark thoughts in this light and lovely place. I admit that the sense of smell is sufficient for gauging the power of my perfume; but the ear will not hear words silently spoken nor will the mind be able to grasp their meaning. May the humility of my glances confess my faults for me; and, if I drop my head, it is to contemplate the cruel moment of my end.

VERSES

When my life approaches its end, a moment of pain and shame and confusion, I will rise up but with my eyes still lowered to the ground, in recognition of the error of my ways. Even if I do make every effort and drive from my eyes the sleep-dust of indifference, I will still have to face the fact of my powerlessness and that I fear to be disappointed in my hope; all the more will I feel it, having slipped so seriously from grace in my past and finding myself tomorrow amongst penitents at the moment of death. What use can I glean from my knowledge and experience, when my eyes have no hope of ever seeing the light of day again? And so, let a salutary fear guide my steps from this day forward! Let us hurry, since haste is inherent in man.

ALLEGORY V
The Water-Lily

Ever sad in hue and languid in looks, the water-lily spoke thus:

You who indulge yourself in sorrow, look closely at my petals' pallor and see if I can hope to escape the unbending decrees of fate. I submit to my misfortune: but I do not renounce love. If you are in love, you, who listen so keenly to my advice, be discreet and act with caution. Gardens are my home and watery places are my bed of rest. My love is for limpid flowing water and I never leave it, morning or evening, wintertime or summertime. And, stranger yet, tormented by my love for this water, I sigh for it ceaselessly, I follow it endlessly, driven without mercy by the burning thirst of desire it inspires in me. But have you ever seen such a thing! To be in water and yet to be consumed by an utterly scorching thirst.

At the dawn of day, I unfold my golden flower-cup and a thousand jealous hands descend on me; but, when night drapes the earth in shadows, the water draws me into itself. Set free, my bowl of petals leans downwards; I immerse myself, and the water rises up to cover me; I retire to my sanctuary of green and return to my solitary thoughts. My bowl, sunk down beneath the water, contemplates, like a watchful eye, the source of its salvation, and heedless people no longer know where I may be.

No troublesome intruder will ever part me from the object of my desire. Besides, wherever my desires take me, I see that water is always with me: if I come asking her to dampen the fire that inflames me, she will give me her gentle liquid to sip; if I ask her for shelter, she will softly take me in. My existence is completely bound to hers, and the life of my flower depends upon her presence, close to mine. In the end, it is only through water that I can reach up to the height of perfection; all worth in me I owe to worth in her. Never will you see me separate from my adored one, for without her I could not, in truth, exist.

VERSES

Love has covered my body with the faded garb of languor; my mind, tortured by the passion which stirs it, is sunk in the blackest of sorrow. When love lets its arrow fly, I always seem to be the first target. The cruel beauty whom I worship only feigns closeness and stirs up in my heart a love that tortures and tears it in two. I live only for her and for her I would die; yes, love itself will make me ready for this glorious death! It says to me, dream only of love if you would enjoy the happiness I hold out to you. At the point of the lance I defend this divinity from anyone's approach; yet it is only if you brave my hidden sting that you will know the delights that I bestow. So do not be distressed by the stabbing wound of the arrow, do not be diverted by the pain; for the end is only happiness. Follow those lovers who died of love for the divine beloved, yet found the fulfilment of their desires. When the children of Israel, prostrate with fatigue from their Red Sea crossing, heard on Mount Sinai these gentle words, 'I am he who is', they had no more regret of their terrible trials and pains.

ALLEGORY VI
The Egyptian Willow

When the trees saw that the willow with its supple boughs was alone forever swaying, they mocked the softness of its swing and spoke harshly of its pride and self-indulgence. Then the willow shook its feathery branches once more and spoke out in the silent language: What is there to reproach me with? Can anyone blame me for my trembling leaves and the shimmering of my branches? It is for me that the earth unrolls its many-coloured carpets, it is for me that the fields unfold their finery and the early morning breath of the zephyr sweetly spreads its delicate aroma. When I notice that plants and flowers are starting to stir, that the earth is moving and coming to life, that the trumpet is sounding the promises made to me by God, the keeping of which dissolves all threats foisted on me, when I see my own blooms are about to open, that the rose has come and the winter has gone, that flowers shine in the most sparkling of colours, the grain is starting to grow and that vegetables destined for the sustenance of man are surging upwards to let him live, then I rise to the knowledge of the Creator, the Lord of all things, and avow that he is unique, almighty, eternal; that he has need of no one yet no one can be without him, let alone take a share in his glorious empire; that he does not beget nor is he begotten and none is like him. It is because I know this that my highest of heights ripple with rejoicing at the inward vision which makes for my delight. It is because of this that the nightingales voice happiness for me on my trembling boughs. Then, through the working of the Grace of God, the source of my faith, I reflect on the very nothingness of my being; and, frightened lest I fail in my purpose, I incline my boughs towards the rose, announcing thus to her my awakening; and while my falling flowers emphasise the elegance of her dress, I ask of her the reason for my existence.

We are exactly alike, she replies: If your branches in bowing would seem to be in prayer to the Most High, mine could be said to be prostrate in adoration; if your beauty lies in the green of your foliage, mine is in the roseate colour of my cheeks. Brother, let us not wait for the eternal fire to consume us; let us throw ourselves into the flames and offer ourselves in sacrifice.

I answered her: If such is your wish, if you pine to perish, I raise no rebuke, and I can bear no separation. We will be torn out together from the very midst of the flowers that are our companions; we will consign ourselves to a scorching fire, whence our spirits will be released but our tears will be made to flow without pity. Our bodies perish but our souls remain; our outward beauty vanishes but our essence lives on; who can doubt the chasm between what we were and what we are now becoming!

VERSES

The rose had already come; she was showing off the loveliness she possesses when the wisp-waisted willow turned toward her in plaint of the violent love that had smitten him; and he gracefully bent to breathe the delights of the perfume she exhaled. The rose, sharer in his pain, said to him: We are close companions and prey to the same ardour; we are as one, our essence is the same. How many times have we not experienced the most terrible torments of the flames? But never has my friend lost sight of the source of his passion, nor have I forgotten the object of mine. How many times, too, have not greedy hands ravished us of our still greening foliage? How hard it is to understand how deeply the cruel flames torment us within and what furnace it is in which our hearts are consumed! Fire separates our spirit from our bodies, it works to sap us of strength. The pain we complain of is the same, although for each of us our loved one seems to be different. I swear by him who rests enthroned for all eternity, and my oath is a true one: from my pain's expression, may all those of sensibility, hearts free of evil, draw substance for reflection: yesterday I was like a rising moon; today I am as a disappearing star.

ALLEGORY VII
The Violet

Then, plaintive with the pain of those seared by separation, the violet sighed and in its secret language spoke these words to me:

How worthy of envy are those who lived their life as happy people and died as martyrs! Why must I fade away pining with grief, my body so slender and sad? The unbending decrees of fate have wasted me, leaving me no texture and no strength; the harsh toll of time has barred me from blooming, dealing me pitiless death. How short were the moments of life's joy for me, how long have I suffered here, sapped and stripped of all my leaves!

As soon as my bud begins to open, people come to pick me and tear me from my roots, leaving me hopeless of reaching full richness: and there is no lack of people to abuse my frailty and handle me with harshness, untouched by my brightness and the beauty of my bloom. I bring joy to those near me, I please those who notice me; but in less than the passing of a single day, I cease to be seen as special; so soon after they have sung my praises, I am sold for the lowest price; so soon after being revered for my riches, I am found to be flawed; in the evening the frowning face of fortune makes my petals curl and fade; in the morning I am no longer lush and lovely.

It is then that I become of interest to medical men, studiously devoted to the natural sciences; it is with my help that they can disperse illness in the body, it is with my help that they can calm chronic pain; they temper the humours and cure many of the ills that beset humanity. When I am fresh, I offer humankind the pleasure of my perfume's sweetness and the charm of my bloom; when faded, I restore them to health. But these very people are oblivious to my most precious of powers; the secrets, insights of God-given wisdom, hidden virtues within me, receive not a passing reflection. Yet for him who would meditate and learn, I am a most suitable case for study; the lessons to be drawn from the way of my life could not fail to touch anyone not deaf to the voice of reason. But alas, my urgings are useless.

VERSES

I looked at the violet with admiration; its flowers on their stalks brought to mind for me an army, an emerald infantry whose sapphire-studded lances could sever the heads of enemies in a single stroke of skill.

ALLEGORY VIII
The Wallflower

Then the wallflower, proud of its colours, spread its own sweet perfume and spoke:

Why let oneself be seduced by the joys of a life that is torn away when least expected? Why ring out in rejoicing for the gift of existence that is cursed a thousandfold with constant misfortune? If you wish to learn, look closely at my drooping stalk, my fading colour, my transient life and the all-too-brief shining of my freshness. The track of time is told in my colouring, once one shade, now three, and each one tells a story.

The first of my flowers wears yellow, the garb of love's sadness; the second shows herself in the white of anxiety, induced by the torments of parting; and the third has a veil of blue, a sign of the sorrow that consumes her. As for the white flower, her petals have no sparkle or scent; people pass her by, senses unstirred, and no one comes to lift the veil which covers up her charms. She purposely keeps her secrets hidden, presses her perfume to herself, so skilled in the shielding of her treasures that no will or wind is wise to them. But the yellow flower sets out to seduce and so she wears a sensual, soporific air, spreading her perfume morning and evening, dawn and sunset releasing the aroma on her breath.

VERSES

Never can the zephyr, soft and full with scented mists, arise from the plain where your beloved tent is standing and not bring me pain that streams the tears from my eyes. Alas, if you did not live in this sacred retreat, no deadly arrow would ever have pierced my breast. You have enslaved my heart! I offer it up to you, I lay down my arms. Oh, do not torment me with the cruelty of more sorrow!

Can you reproach me for confiding my pain to the zephyr when I am so pressed by the desires of love?

Do not blame me, O my brother, when I tell of the ardour that may be my downfall. The lover who betrays his secret is guiltless, broken open only by the force of his desires.

*   *   *

As for my blue flower, it suppresses its passion, bears its pain with patience and never breathes forth perfume in the daylight hours. It says: while the sun spreads its light, my secret stays hidden from those who love me and I lavish no scent on those who would smell it; but as soon as the night veils me in its shadows, I open the treasures to my friends and weep of my pain to those who suffer the same grief. When the drinking-cups are passed around, I drink in my turn; and when the moment seems right, I exhale my night breath and spread for those close to me a scent as sweet as the company of a comforting friend.

Every time that my presence is sought, I assent at once to the invitation; and whenever I suffer at the hands of the hard-hearted, I make my plaint only to God. Do you know why I withhold my perfume by day and remove my veil only at night? It is because lovers choose for their rendezvous the darkness and the mistress waits till dark to show herself to her lover. At this happy moment, no rival makes his troublesome presence felt, nothing stands in the way of access to the divine friend; so as soon as she shows a concern for her lovers, I send her my sighs, like so many love-letters, and let my humility itself speak for me.

VERSES

I send to my mistress the burning sighs of my love, I waft her with my awe. That sweet moment of happiness at which I aim can only be won if my humility and purity of purpose can speak for me; I have no other intermediary. Whether my friend accepts my homage or rejects it (I am powerless in that), my love, at least, will never waver.

ALLEGORY IX
The Jasmin

With an eloquence evoked by its silent language, the jasmin then said this:

Despair is an error. My penetrating perfume eclipses the scent of the other flowers so that lovers choose me to offer to their mistress. I am drawn from the invisible treasure of divinity, yet my resting-place in the end is on a pin that holds a dress in folds across the breast.

Whoever's heart is open to the charms of a life spent in contemplation will know that the air is ever sweetened by my breath. Whoever is at a powerful love's mercy can never by blind to my bloom. My perfume, I repeat it, eclipses that of all flowers, the scented breath that escapes from my breast surpasses that of all others.

Only he who is truly pure is truly religious; and if he is what he aspires to be, he is worthy of eminence and distinction. You who desire to reach the heights of inner knowledge, look to earn merit and acquire virtues, these are rungs on the ladder of inner life; but if you dare not step down the path of the mystic, do not look for that especial protection that truth grants to those who embark upon it.

My name is a riddle; its meaning can only please those new to the spiritual life; it is made up of two words, *yas*, despair and *min*, error. But despair is an error and error is shame; yet when despair and error are united, they signify the end of misfortune, they forecast felicity and joy.

VERSES

In the receiving of jasmin, I am given an omen of happiness ahead of me. Cease to sorrow, for sorrow is tinged with shame; and do not despair. For despair is itself an error.

ALLEGORY X
The Basil

Now, said the basil, is the moment when my flower adorns your garden; therefore give me your orders and take me as one of your party. My fresh, delicate leaves themselves bespeak my rare qualities; just as dancing would be dull without the sound of instruments, so the spirit could not be gladdened without me, who serve to give it strength. I am promised a place with the elect in paradise; of all colours, the most harmonious is mine; in form I have no equal. A precious perfume is locked in my breast; penetrating to the innermost heart, it is known to those who come to pick me from my flowerbed. I am friend of the streams, companion of flowers. I share the secrets that are told by moonlight and I am the most faithful guardian of their tellers. You may have heard, however, that among my relatives there exists an informer (the mint); but I ask of you not to reproach him; he has only his own scent to spread, the only secret that he shares is his own, what he reveals is what he has discovered himself. If he has treasures to show, it is his right to lay them open to daylight; if he spreads forth his smell, is he then forbidden to put to it his name? Yet this is all that has earned him the injurious name of informer! To be indiscreet about oneself is not comparable to indiscretions with others' secrets; nor can the man who is prodigal with his own possessions be compared to those whose perversity does evil to all. Be that as it may, all men agree, nothing is more worthy of blame than the forfeit of trust. Think of it, my brother, and farewell.

VERSES

O you who would penetrate the secret of my love, cease striving, I beseech you, and leave me to my passion! The sweet secret confided to me by my friend I received in trust, so why would you have me divulge it? I do not speak out of my turn.

ALLEGORY XI
The Camomile

Enchanted with its own delights, the camomile sang its own

praises in these words:

Now is the time of my coming, now is the season when I add my finery to the fields, when my leaves are full green and my beauty is all the softer and more pleasing. How could the days when my flower is open be anything other than delight? These streams, named so often in the Koran, do they not come to bathe my stems? My annual charity, how could I fail to pay it gladly, since, without any effort of my own, I am the beneficiary of all that surrounds me? No, it is my welcome duty to pay. My white petals make me stand out from afar, while my centre is a soft, languid yellow. The contrast between these colours can be compared to the contrast between verses of the Koran; some are clear and others are subtle.

If you have the ability to understand these symbols, rise up and take profit from those that are offered you; if not, then sleep, since you cannot perceive what nature is spreading out for you here in her charms; but let it be known that such ignorance can have no excuse.

VERSES

Do not lay the blame on me if you cannot grasp the hidden meaning of what I tell you and if you do not understand the mystery of the emblems that I use. It is purely through compassion for you that I speak in the expressive language of allegory. But I speak in vain, your ear is deaf to the lessons that I teach. What, can you not extract at least some useful instruction from my seeming death, which happens every year, from cruel torments which fate makes me suffer? You have often come to admire me when my open flower shone with the softest brilliance; you came soon again, but you did not then find me. When I tell my sorrows to the doves of the woodlands, they lighten my troubles and seem to echo my lamentations, for they are not blind to the thousand deaths I may die.

You take this plaint of pain to be a song of pleasure and desire, and it is joy you experience as you stand on the lawn that is studded with my flowers. Alas. Too bad if you can't tell my gladness from my sorrow!

ALLEGORY XII
The Lavender

When the wild lavender saw the trials and torment suffered by the flowers, either pressed into bunches or left lying, abandoned in contempt, she said:

Oh, how lucky I am not to be a bloom that decorates the flower-beds. I run no risk of falling into vile hands and I am spared the comments of critics. Contrary to the custom with other flowers, nature has me growing far away from streams and far from moist, grassy hills. Like wild animals, I keep well away from civilisation, the desert and the wilderness ever my home; I like to be in isolated places, I am never one of a crowd. Since no one sows me or tends me, no one can reproach me with any care spent on me.

I am not picked by the hand of a slave nor am I given to the gambler or the vain or frivolous man. If you come to Najd, you will find me there; there, far from human dwellings, I have a vast plain to make me happy, the absinthe is my company, my solitary pleasure the gazelle. The wind picks up my perfume and carries it to those devout ones who have, like me, retired from the world, and spend their time only in pious exercise; I can say that only those smell my scent who have a passion for the contemplative life and, filled with a true and burning love, have the piety of the Messiah, the patience of Ishmael. Morning and evening, I am companion to the pilgrim who crosses the desert. The company I enjoy is that of good people, I am sheltered from the bad. I am not forced to take part in illicit meetings and I am never near to men who drink themselves senseless. I am like a free man, who can never be bought. I am never put up for sale in the markets, like a hypocrite who counterfeits his religion. I am not sought after by libertines, but appreciation I receive from those who, with an unshakeable resolution, wholeheartedly take determination by the reins and guide it towards spiritual things. I wish you could be in the desert when, close to me, the morning breeze blows up and down the valleys. The fresh sweetness of my scent is the perfume of the solitary bedouin; my moist breath gladdens the senses of those lying close to me. When the camel driver extols my rare virtues to the parties in passing caravans, they cannot help but feel moved and mindful of my merits.

VERSES

The zephyr comes to carry me sweet words from the lavender and greetings from the absinthe. My love is crowned with success: I gather this from their figurative speech. Happy state! May it last forever! The breeze moves on in to the mystery of night and, while my companions are in a deep sleep, it wakes me gently. Its scented and refreshing breath stirs feelings in me which intoxicate me. The zephyr, ever laden with sweet-smelling scents and, by divine grace, possessed of finest qualities, surrounds me with its humming breath, that echoes my sighs of love; and my passion takes strength anew. I wander in search of that perfumed wind, immersed in the purest of joy and love, and the very lightning seems to smile at my raptures. The zephyr passes through the countryside of Najd and, as if in respect, the bending branches bow before him. By their plaintive cooing, the doves of the neighboring grove remind me of those beloved tents and pavilions to which so many eager lovers run to receive the reward for their steadfast love; it is there that the idol, invoked by my sighs, unveils that radiance whose spendour dispels the darkness of the night.

ALLEGORY XIII
The Anemone

The anemone, which, even in the very midst of its companions, is branded by its petals' blood-red tint, now gave a sigh and, straightening its stem, seemed to speak these words:

Why are the praises lavished on other flowers so rarely given to me, when my beauty is radiant and my colour so pleasing to the eye? Why? No one tells my charms, no one wishes to pick me. What is the cause of this marked indifference? I feel proud of the rich colours of my garment, yet those who catch sight of me then disregard me; I have no place in the drawing-room vases; and worse than that, my sheen and my scent seem equally obnoxious. Among the flowers which decorate the flower beds I am given only the last place and even *they* throw me out of their midst and bar me from their gentle companionship. As I see it, all this can only be because my heart is base; but what can I do to fight the decrees of providence! So, seeing that I am full of flaws within and that my heart is tarnished by vices, and knowing that the All-High pays attention to inner qualities, not to outer form, I realise that my very pleasure in my own striking beauty is why divine favour is denied me.

I am like the hypocrite, whose outward behaviour is beyond reproach but whose soul harbours vileness: outwardly, his merits deserve lauding to the skies, inwardly he is but nothing. If within I could be as I am without, I should have no cause for complaint and, if God willed, I could be an object of respect and could offer to the senses a heady fragrance; but good can come only from those who are truly good. And so it is that only they wear the signs of grace whose homage has been accepted by the divine mistress. Let them lament their pain and shed countless tears, those sunk in sorrow at the scorn of their divine friend, those who will never know the true essence of this divine beauty.

VERSES

Do not blame me if I tear my clothes; your reproaches would only make worse the pain I suffer because of love. The errors of my ways have blackened my soul and a bitter fate has sentenced me to misfortune. Those who see me admire me. But alas! My creator knows that I harbour the heart of a hypocrite: outwardly I am beauty itself but vices are hidden in my guilty breast. Shame of the last day when I step forward for questioning! Alas, I will have no excuses to bring. Oh, if you were to lift the veil that hides my baseness, you would see joy reflected on the faces of those that hate me.

ALLEGORY XIV
The Cloud

When the moment seemed right for the cloud to speak in its silent language, it shed some tears, spread its wispy pillow and, floating in the hazy air, it seemed to say these words:

Plants, can you be oblivious to the prize that I pour on you, I who help you grow by my shade and showers! Are you not the children of my bounty? Could you even exist without me? Thanks to my giving, are the fields not covered with golden ears of corn, is the sea not a-shimmer with sparkling pearls?

When you are only germs of plants, I feed you in your mothers' bosom and slowly I free you of all that would hinder your growth. Later, like a pregnant woman, the seeds bring forth their own and it is I who help them take shoot from their sandy shallows, I who promise them care and give them nurture; like the udder of the camel heavy with milk, my breast ceaselessly pours forth favours, willing them the water that is vital for their growth. But when suckling is over and weaning-time comes, I bar them from my breast; but then they soon shrivel and only the copiousness of my tears revives them, only the waterfall of my weeping gives them back freshness once more. All beings that exist are in truth my children; does not every tribe know this passage from the Koran: "To every creature we have given life by means of water!"

VERSES

When I look upon this spring pavilion, my mistress's former

home, empty today and uninhabited, I cannot help shedding tears akin to those of your soft showers. While the lover lets fall tears of joy, the lightning seems to smile and the zephyr, carrier of hope, brings sweet news to his ear; he then sighs with love, turning towards the half-crumbled ruins that formed his lady's home. Don't reproach him his love, do not point down his passion, you can bring no remedy for his ills. As for you, cast aside these violent desires; a burning passion, a consuming grief, is all that you would reap.

ALLEGORY XV
The Nightingale

As I sat by the river which wound through the garden, intent upon the wordless speech of the flowers which enriched it, eloquent voices suddenly arose from the swaying nests in the tops of the trees, in whose shade I was sitting. First I heard the melodic tones of the nightingale which, set to seduce by the beauty of his song, now gave voice to the secrets he had carefully concealed. His enigmatic warbling seemed to lisp these words:

I am a lover in the throes of passion, drunk with love, devoured by melancholy and consumed by the thirst of desire.

When you see spring come and the whole of nature starts to smile, that is when you will find me in the gardens, brimful with joy; that is when you will catch sight of me here and there in the groves, sighing my love, singing my song and flitting constantly through the branches.

If I am offered the cup, I quench my thirst and, happy with the harmonious tones of my voice, intoxicated by the balmy scents that I breathe, I sway with the rhythm of the branches whose wavering leaves tremble at the zephyr's caress; the flowers and the stream that crosses the grassland are ever in my consciousness, an endless source of joy. And because of this you imagine that I am some lighthearted lover. You are wrong; to this I swear and I do not swear lightly. My song has the tune of suffering, not joy. The sounds that I make are cadences of sorrow, not those of rapture.

Every time that I loiter awhile in a garden, my murmuring message is of the affliction so soon to replace the gaiety that reigns there. If I am in a pleasant place, I lament its imminent destruction; if I see a brilliant gathering, I grieve at its dissolution. For never have I known of a joy that lasts; the sweetest peace is soon disturbed, the most idyllic life will all too soon turn sour. Be sure, I have read these very words: "Everything passes in this world". How, then, not to bewail all things so uncertain, an existence exposed to the shiftings of fortune, a life that fades, an instant of ecstasy so soon snuffed out? This is why I act as I do. I think you can accept it.

VERSES

All that has meaning for me in my life is my chance to speak of that sacred place, the unapproachable arbour of the one whom I adore. Do not blame me for ceaselessly repeating my songs of love; what mere mortal could fail to be intoxicated at the thought of a garden where strong-scented plants fragrantly perfume the air; where delicious wines set the senses astir, where the ground is a multi-coloured carpet of flowers unsurpassed in charm and beauty, here snow-white or brilliant red, there softest green and yonder deepest yellow! It is as if the stream, flowers and branches move to the sound of my lyre's strings in the sanctuary of my love. Burdens cease to bar the way and at last I can perceive the coming of that moment of bliss . . . Sweet thoughts, you are my life; without you it would be nothing.

ALLEGORY XVI
The Falcon

From the grounds of the hunt the falcon at once spoke out:

For someone as tiny in size as you, he said to the nightingale, you are hugely errant in your ways: your ceaseless singing tires the other birds; it is the excesses of your utterings that draw misfortunes upon you and you fail to learn from your lot. Are you unaware that man himself is lost by those very thoughts of which the tongue is guilty? Indeed, were it not for your tactless utterances, you would never be torn from your companions and imprisoned in the narrow confines of a cage; nor would the door of deliverance be ever now closed to you. Tell me, are the misfortunes that cover your eloquence with shame not rooted in your tongue?

If, on the other hand, you took me for your model and tried to keep your own counsel, as I do, then you would be above reproach; then you would realise that this worthy quality is the lifeline to salvation.

Look at me! See how faithful I am to the rules of silence. What do I say! Merit for me is the very discretion of my tongue, my perfection the observance of my duties. Though by force I have been torn away from the desert and brought against my will to a far-off land, never do you find me revealing my deepest thoughts; nor will you see me weeping over remnants that remind me of a loved one. Instruction is what I seek on my journey; and I have been found fit for reward whenever I have been put to the test; for according to the proverb, it is the test that decides whether someone is worth honour or contempt. When perceiving the treachery of time and fearing that hatred may move me, my master covers my eyes with the hood, I understand his actions by the words: Do not extend your sight. The gag he uses to tie my tongue, is explained thus: Do not be free with your tongue; and the shackles he binds me with also find allusion in the admonition: Do not walk the earth with petulance in your step. I suffer from being bound this way, yet I do not complain of the ills I endure.

When my eyes have long been covered by the hood and I have learned what is deemed I need know, when I have come through my trials and developed some skill, then my master is happy to use me for the hunt.

Delivering me from my bonds, he throws me, making the signal that appears in the Koran, when God said to the Prophet: "We sent you". The hood is only removed from my eyes when I am adept in executing what I have been taught; it is then that kings become my servants and their wrists are beneath my proud feet.

VERSES

I forbid my tongue an excess of speech, I forbid my eyes the spectacle of the world: menacing death, each day ever closer, makes me oblivious to the sweetest raptures. My only concern is to make my own the manner of princes and to practise noble acts. It is from the king's wrist I take off for my flight; aiming for my prey, I seize it at once in my victorious talons and am ready, at the slightest sign, to return to Him who sent me.

My life should serve as a guide for all those who would bow to the sacred laws of submission to faith.

ALLEGORY XVII
The Dove

Still absorbed by the welcome words of the falcon, I was meditating on the lessons of wisdom and prudence he had given me when I saw before him a dove in the collar of obedience. I said to her: tell of your 'tasting' and of your 'yearning'; reveal the purpose of Providence to me, in adorning you with that beautiful chain. She replied:

The carrying of tender messages that win hearts is my charge, and my faithful completion of the tasks entrusted to me is signified by this collar. Indeed, if I may speak frankly, since religion wills sincerity, not every bird is deserving of trust, just as an oath is not always an assurance of truth and not every taker of the spiritual path is assuredly of the elect.

My kind alone does exactly as told and my integrity is proved by this proverb: black-and-white birds, as well as green ones, faithfully deliver whatever is entrusted them, for their inner form is as superior as their outward bearing.

A bird that is black is not fitted for the function, while all-whiteness is the sign of some deep imperfection, an apathy that prevents him from doing what needs to be done. (Noble aims and aspirations are found only in pure and noble unswerving souls.) But when the colour of a bird is a perfect blend of both, as a carrier he is peerless and should be raised up to this role. He can be bought where merchants cry their wares, in markets, and be brought to gradual awareness of his way. So, whenever I offer to carry a message, do not be loath to put letters, filled with secrets, in my care or to trust me with pleasant tidings.

I set off; but soon my mind is racked with worry; for I must avoid the bloodthirsty bird of prey, that swift traveller and merciless hunter. So I speed my flight, ignoring scorching thirst in the southern deserts, cold to cruel hunger in the rocky wastes. Yes, should I even catch sight of a grain of wheat, I hasten onwards, despite my great need, ever mindful that it was wheat that brought terrible misfortune on Adam. And, in my fear of failing to arrive with the letter, thus becoming a party to dire deception, I take great care to escape ensnarement, in nets hidden by dust or in perfidious lakes. As soon as I reach my desired journey's end, and find myself secure in safety, I relinquish my load and act as I have been taught. So now you see why I am graced with a collar. I was born to be bearer of happy tidings and I thank God that he chose me.

VERSES

Beloved friend, may I hope for even the smallest favour or have you grown weary of me? Whatever you say, the slave of your beauty will not fail to be faithful; he is not swayed by censorious sentiments; and nothing could make him renounce his noble passion. For the sake of your love even the loftiest peaks do not daunt me. Yes, I shall stay loyal to the sermon I swore to you. Keeping faith with one's promises is the finest trait that can grace a well-born man.

Let him surrender to the love of the beauty who holds him captivated; for your lot is the same as his, O you who reproach him so cruelly.

ALLEGORY XVIII
The Swallow

As I talked with the dove of the qualities which one needs to acquire perfection and how to perfect these qualities, I glimpsed a swallow wheeling around, above a cottage; at once I said to her: It always surprises me to see you near houses, seeking out the companionship of man; would it not be wiser to keep with your kind, to savour sweet freedom in the fields instead of shackling yourself to our dwellings? Why do you settle close to civilisation, in places inhabited by man?

She replied:

Since your thoughts are so unsubtle and you are so hard of hearing, let me try to tell you why I do what I do and why I cannot keep company with other birds. If I have abandoned my own kind, if I have sought out beings of another species, if I have chosen the rooftops to be my home, not the boughs and the hollows of trees, it is because, in my eyes, there is nothing so alluring as an alien way of living, one of elegant manners that I wish to acquire. I mingle with beings who are not of my kind because that allows me to be the stranger; I seek the company of my betters so that I may benefit from the goodness within.

By continuously living the life of the wanderer, I have contact with learned folk. And the stranger, far from home, is always treated with kindness, the recipient of courtesy and charm. When I settle on a house, it is with care that its owners are in no way inconvenienced; I confine myself to building my cell, made from things that I find by the side of streams, and only in deserted places do I look for food.

Never do I harm him whose home I share; far from it, whenever there is a crossing of paths, I stand by all courtesies that one neighbour must show to another. And yet he does not provide my keep. By my presence, I swell the size of the household, but I do not ask to take a share in their bread; careful to claim no part of their goods, I am assured of their affections. For, if I wanted to divide their food with them, they would drive me from their homes. I keep their company but I leave when they dine. I join them in prayer but never at their meals.

I wish to partake of their fineness, not their food; it is their inner qualities I covet, not their outward show; their worth, not their wheat, is what I seek. It is their friendship I desire, not their grain.

I model my behaviour on the words of the one to whom the Almighty deigned to reveal His will (may God look on him kindly and grant him salvation): If you can pass by the pleasures of this world, you will enjoy the friendship of God; if you can pass by the possessions of men, you will win their affections . . .

VERSES

Yes, shun the possessions of others and everyone will love you. Do you not see the swallow! She never touches our provisions; so we welcome her home, like a ward that one hugs to one's heart.

*   *   *

It was a pleasure to hear your eloquent speech, I said to the swallow: How fortunate you are. Your reasoned conduct is worthy of praise. Your words are filled with wisdom and I will take heed. Farewell.

ALLEGORY XIX
The Owl

A moment later the owl spoke up from his sad retreat in a

solitary hovel:

True and sincere friend, do not listen to the swallow, nor try to live as she lives. For, though none could suspect her of feeding from your table, it is certainly true that she steals a share in your pleasures, your joys, your celebrations, it is true that she lives in your midst.

Now, as you will know, anyone who mingles with people cannot help but become a part of those people; however short his stay, he will have learnt much of their ways; just as a single drop of rain is the unsuspected source of a raging torrent, so is society the root of crime; no place is it, then, to invest one's happiness.

Only in retreat are true happiness and peace to be found. Ah, he who takes refuge there need never fear the distractions of envy!

Follow my example and look for loneliness: leave the sumptuous palaces and those who live in them; discard all delicacies and those who eat them. Take heed of what I do. I do not live in your houses, or take part in your gatherings. A hole in a crumbling wall is my solitary abode, and I would rather have ruins than places that are tended by man. There, far from companions, my friends and my intimates, I am safe from torment, protected from pain and have nothing to fear from the envious. How can he whose dwelling will one day turn to dust carry on living with other men? Each new day and night takes new tolls of his life, yet he will not be content with a hovel. He who has the fortune to understand that life, which seems long, is really so short and that all that moves onward moves on to destruction, will choose a hard mat as his couch, instead of the night-time luxury of a bed; he will be content to have barley-flour bread as his food and will shun, when he can, the pleasures of the world, mindful that paradise will become home for some, while others are thrown into hell.

For my part, I have looked at this life and have seen that devastation is imminent; I have then turned my gaze to the life that comes after and have seen that it is almost upon us. Remembering, then, God's terrible calling to account on the Judgment Day, I began to meditate upon the soul, its potential for goodness, its capacity for evil. It was then, as I reflected upon my life and thought deeply about myself, that I decided to abandon a world whose offerings were all empty; I forgot my duties towards my kind, I forgot their duties towards me; I forsook my family and my possessions, I laughed at the lofty castles. Soon faith took the blindfold of doubt from my mind's eye and I knew that no joy or pleasure can ever abide; that everything perishes, bar the Being to whom all owe their existence. I have raised myself to knowledge of this Being, though I can never know Him. His adored image is all that my eyes perceive, my mouth can only intone his blessed name.

VERSES

For this divine friend, I have abandoned mankind; she alone is my desire, she alone I yearn to please. For her sake, all society I shun and, guided by most true intent, I surrender myself to the purest form of Love. I shall see her, I shall hope for her; my love will not be in vain. My friends have reproached my heart's noble passion, ignorant of the feeling that fires it. Should the object of my ardour lift the veil that hides her beauty, the glow would be such as to silver the moon. My respect does not let me dare name this divinity who elicits only awe from all men. But when my violent passion can no longer be constrained, my sighs spill forth some of her glory.

*   *   *

I eagerly listened to the owl's advice and stripped myself of self-love; but my passions seemed to whisper: Stay, stay with me.

ALLEGORY XX
The Peacock

Turning aside I saw a peacock: in drinking to the dregs from the cup of vanity and donning a dissembling cloak, that bird is a mirror of the misdeeds of the demon, Eblis. His plumage is made sumptuous by its shifting colours but his life lays him open to a thousand kinds of suffering and never will he see paradise again (the reason being known to God).

Unfortunate bird, I said to him, how different is the fate allotted to you from that which destiny holds for the owl. All the owl's thought is for real, inner qualities while you are bewitched by external forms; you have let yourself be duped by ephemeral existence, your happiness hangs on all that cannot last.

Frail mortal who insults me, he replied, cease your reproaches and refrain from reminding one burdened with grief of what has been taken from him. Have pity on the famous one who is stripped of his distinction, have pity on the wealthy who finds that he is poor! Would that you had seen me, when I walked in Eden, stepping between limpid streams and the mellow clusters of fruits that graced it; when, free to wander, I passed inside its splendid palaces and rejoiced in the company of comely cup-bearers and voluptuous houris. I drank the praises of God; the celebration of his sanctity was my sustenance. And so it was, until my fatal destiny drew me towards Eblis, who clothed me in the cloak of hypocrisy and dulled my shining qualities to faults. At first I was horrified by his proposal. But alas! If Destiny so wishes, it wreaks havoc and misfortune, causing birds to flee their nests, even to cast themselves to the hunter.

As for Eblis, his walk was proud and his dress was the celestial clothing of God's favour; but, in the end, his own evil destiny was the way of arrogance and he refused to prostrate himself before Adam. It was after the event of his refusal that I had the misfortune to mix with this rebel angel.

He led me to crime, concealing from me the perversity of his plan; yes, indeed, I acted as his guide in Eden, while his ally the snake plotted for his ascendency. After it all, God cast me down from the land of glory to the dwelling of disgrace, alongside of Adam and Eve and Eblis and the snake. And He said to me: This is the reward he receives who serves as guide for an evil deed; this is the price you deserve to pay for working with the wicked. God left me my plumes, emboldened by a thousand hues, a beauty that evokes the charmed life of Eden and adds to my regrets, my desires, my moans. But as the sign of his anger he branded me with ugly feet, so that every time I unthinkingly cast down my eyes I remember my betrayal of duty.

How I love these valleys where all nature's charms merge to remind me of the place from where I was cast out and from which I shall ever by parted by the cruelty of my fate! Pleasant gardens recall for me the springtime meadows of my former home and my eyes shed for it a myriad of tears; it is then, more than ever, that I repent my errant ways and cry out in my grief.

VERSES

Delightful place, may I ever hope to see you again? Will an instant of peaceful sleep in your bosom ever be mine to enjoy? O, you who live in those blessed places, when I bade my very last farewell at the cruel moment of parting, I was almost dead with pain and chagrin. Will you never feel compassion for my hapless condition? You have driven the sleep from my eyes and bound me forever to my affliction;my body is far from you, but my spirit is there among your tents; why may my body not join my spirit there? If my torrents of tears did not wash my pain when I call to mind the lovely nights spent in ravishing places, under protecting pavilions, I should die consumed of desire. In my reverie, I thought that you promised to come and visit your faithful friend. Alas, my ardour was fired, my desire grew greater. If this painful separation is due to a fault of which I have been guilty, may my sad state today speak in my favour. But, alas! Forever past are those sweet moments and my lot is submission and modesty.

*   *   *

And I, moved as I was by the peacock's misfortunes, shed tears for his pain. I feel, yes, that no pain is greater than emptiness, when once one has enjoyed the fruits of the sweetest union; and nothing is more bitter than the veiling of charms that in joyful adoration one once was free to see.

ALLEGORY XXI
The Parakeet

And so the peacock sighed as he looked at his plumage, the reminder of his happiness, or cried a plaintive cry of pain when his eyes were drawn down to his feet. And there beside him I saw a parakeet, her green raiment a mark of her delicateness. She spoke to the peacock in this elegant way:

How long will you wear that sombre air? Your superb plumage is like a young bride's gown but is, in reality, the darkness of the tomb.

Your wrong judgment led you to be expelled from the place of delights you knew; this is how you have been handled for your treachery towards man, who was living in the sacred abode, and for disturbing a happiness which should have been without end.

If you gave thought to your banishment and to man, who was the cause, surely you would spend your time atoning for your wrongs, not gadding about in a garden?

Since you are guilty of doing Adam wrong in Eden, you should now be working to redeem yourself! Go and join him in his retreat, as he addresses fervent prayers to God, imploring clemency, and admit the fault you at first refused to acknowledge, in the hope of one day, with the father of men, visiting the celestial palaces; for Adam, without fail, will return to his original state and happiness will be restored to him.

Indeed, this is what was said to him, when he was put down on the grass in this world, upon his expulsion from Eden: Sow today what will be reaped tomorrow, even though *you* may not gather the fruit; and then, when all the sowing is done and your plants have begun to grow, return to the happy place you came from, despite the hostile and the envious.

Fortunate will he be who follows the example you set by your penitence; he who borrows from your behaviour will be rewarded with eternity for his home.

Do you not see in what esteem I am held when my thoughts are lofty, soaring? Disdaining the diversions of the other birds, I have given my thought to the world and its creatures and I have realised it is man upon whom I should model myself. For all other beings God created for man whilst man He created for Himself. He has attached them to Himself with indissoluble bonds and has showered them with special favours. So, even though my nature is so different, I have tried to adopt their way of life, especially speaking in their speech and eating the foods they eat. It is my happiness to speak to them; them alone I seek out; and it is my efforts to emulate them that ensure for me the esteem in which they hold me; they consider me as one of their household; and a mutual friendship unites us. Bending my way to theirs, I pray as they pray and give thanks as they do.

I am entitled to hope that they will remember me and speak well of me on the day when they appear before God; so that, having been numbered among their servants in this world, I may also be their slave in the next.

VERSES

If you seek to know me you will see I am one who really is what I seem to be. The object of my passions is a beauty possessed of brilliant and sublime perfections. She is graced with purity and sanctity of heart and her highest rank is awed and blessed. Yes, I have hope that my wishes will be granted: Mahommed, the most excellent of men, whose words could not be other than true, affirms that the lover will be united with his beloved.

*　　*　　*

This eulogy of her qualities having won for the parakeet a place in the highest circle, I said to myself: I had never studied what was signified by the ways of the animals, yet what do I see today? They are awake while I lie in the deepest sleep of apathy and indifference. Why should I not make my way to the door of the Merciful? Perhaps this clement God may allow me access and say to me these comforting words: "Welcome is he who comes to me. I forgive his wrongs who repents."

ALLEGORY XXII
The Bat

Soon after this, the sleepy trembling bat addressed me in these words:

Do not mingle with the crowd if you yearn for the favours of the divine beauty whom you cherish. In olden times, Sham loitered long by the sacred retreat but it was only Sem whom God allowed to enter.

VERSES

It is not the blackened lance that makes us the masters of the ends we desire; it is not by the sword that we reach to higher things.

*   *   *

One must devote time to retreat and spend dark nights in fervent prayer. Heed what I do. With the sunrise, I retire to my solitary hole; there my mind, free of all care, surrenders to sweet thoughts. As long as the day lasts, alone, out of sight, in the recesses of my cell, I venture to visit none, and no one visits me. And yet, enlightened people love me and hold me in esteem. But when night has draped the earth in its shadows, I venture forth from my corner and elect at this time to be wakeful and to act.

It is in the deep of the shadows that the sacred doors open, the much looked-for lifting of the veil occurs and, jealous rivals unaware, the beloved receives her favourite ones alone. On the very instant that lovers of this celestial beauty, and those unfortunates consigned to this land of exile, find their burning eyes filled with tears, she parts the curtain and shows herself upon that blessed threshold.

She summons her worshippers herself and grants them audience in secret. And it is then that they address fervent prayers to her, faltering in their weeping. And it is then that they are given the joy of hearing these sweet words: "Celestial messenger, let this one sleep but make that other wake. Tell the lover who kept his burning passion for me hidden that he may now make bold to speak it; say to this thirsty lover that the cup is full; tell him whose love has plunged him into turbulence that the wondrous moment of union with his loved one has come."

VERSES

O you whose noble passion has no other object but me, do not let reproaches drive you forth from the threshold of my door; for pledges must be lasting and love must be constant. The fame of my power, my beauty and my favours has spread through all the universe and the pilgrims have started on their journey. If you submit to my supreme dignity, sovereigns and monarchs will respectfully yield to yours. O lovers! Hasten! Here are the charger and the hippodrome.

* * *

Tiny, frail flyer, I then said to the bat, tell me why it is that you cease to see when the sun comes up and regain your sight only when it sets; how is it that this star, from which others draw light, brings to you only blindness?

Unfortunate mortal, she replied, until this time I have been busy with finding the true path and I still lack the virtues that would make me worthy to embark on it; whoever is in this state of searching and fear is dazzled by the light of the stars of spirituality; but he who has the virtues of inner life can contemplate the mysteries God deigns to reveal to him.

My condition of weakness, hesitation and doubt is due to negligence in fulfilling my duties. This is why I hide my imperfections by day and conceal myself from sight. But when night envelops the earth in its shadows, I talk with humility in secret to my friend who, moved by my misery, generously draws me from the dejection into which I have fallen.

The first kindness this celestial mistress showed me, the first favour she granted to my humble prayers, was to assign me the night as the time of sweetest meeting, and to let me join her lovers in raising my eyes towards her. And so, when those precious moments are passed, I close my eyes to shut out all others. After all, it is only right that he who has been awake all night should sleep during the day; and for eyes that have enjoyed a vision divine, it would be a crime to glance towards another object.

VERSES

A heart consumed by love for its celestial friend should beat for none other. Could you love this divine beauty and then make a vow to another? Do you not know that this alone in the world is worthy of being loved? Brother, since the one you love is without equal, if you love truly, then be without equal in your love.

ALLEGORY XXIII
The Cockerel

Those who enjoy special favours from God are fortunate indeed, I then said to myself. Those who spend their time in prayer deserve to be distinguished from others. There is no way the indifferent could ever approach this divine mistress. So I was reflecting when the cockerel spoke to me in these words:

How often have I called you to your religious duties while

you stayed blinded by passions and deluded by the senses!

It is my charge to make the call to prayer, to awaken those who sleep the deep sleep of the dead and bring joy to those others who in humility and fear invoke their God. Of my behaviour you may make these allegories: the beating of my wings tells the time to rise for prayer, while the ringing of my voice serves to stir those still asleep; in the flapping of my wings I speak happiness and use my song as a summons to the temple of salvation. If the bat has elected to make good of the night, she spends the whole day in the deepest sleep, hiding herself in fear from the eyes of men; but I, I never take rest from the demands of my duties, neither by day nor by night; never do I shirk them, publicly or in private.

I divide the duties of service to God through the different hours of the day and never one passes without my fulfilling some religious requirement. It is I who make known to you the hours set for prayer. Indeed, might I say, I could never be bought for my real value, were my weight to be paid in rubies. And besides, in my fond affection for my young, I am always near them and, in their midst, love engrosses me only. True to the ruling of genuine affection, no merest morsel of food, no slight sip of liquid is taken without my companions. Far from keeping it for myself if I see a grain, I present it to them and beseech them to take it for food. So, also, I invite them to eat when I smell the aroma of what has been prepared for us. For the rest, obedient to the people of the house, I bear with patience the suffering they cause me. Gentle friend to them am I, yet they have the cruelty to sacrifice my young. I act for their good, yet they take my faithful womenfolk away from me. These are the qualities and kindness that mark me. For me, God's love is enough.

VERSES

Call on God and you will be sheltered from all fear. Trust in him and you will find happiness. But alas! Who knows how to give ear to what I say, who can grasp its full meaning and etch it into his memory?

ALLEGORY XXIV
The Duck

The duck that was dabbling in the water spoke to the cockerel thus: O you with your thoughts so vile and base, you cannot, like the other birds, even take to the air, nor save yourself by avoiding misfortune; like a dead man, you are unable to travel the earth and your plight is all caused by your hovering round a permanent home! Your base inclinations make you look for waste; and, content merely to collect the dew, you neglect the copious rain. Do you not know that he who does not travel will never make a profit in his trade? And that he who stays close to the shore will never bring up pearls? If your spiritual worth were real and if your faith were stronger, you would fly in the sky and you would glide on water. See how, as master of my desires and adept in both air and water, I can walk on the earth and fly freely through ethereal domains. Beyond all, it is the sea that is the seat of my power and the mine of my treasure: I throw myself into its limpid translucent waters. I discover the precious pearls it holds and I penetrate the mysteries and wonders of God. Only he who exerts his spiritual will can know these things; but the indifferent man, who remains on the shore, will know only the bitter foam. He who plunges into this ocean without thought for its unfathomable depths will be drawn down into its whirlpool by the violence of the waves! But the man destined for happiness is taken on board of his divine friend's charity, unfurls the sails of his supplication, steers them to catch the breath of the protective zephyr and, once across the shadowed deep that hides the mysteries, drawn by His attraction-powers he ties the cable of hope at the very point where the two seas, the sea of qualities and the sea of essence, meet. And so he arrives at the very fount of existence itself, where he drinks of water that is sweeter than the purest honey.

VERSES

O you who wish to reach the highest spirituality, you will find it hard to achieve the perfection for which you hope. If you step on the way, all too soon you must submit to utter annihilation, a nothingness which can only become sweet to those whom God has given a glimpse of what He holds for his favourites. The approach-road to this celestial beloved is guarded by the spearhead and the lofty citadels are surrounded by a daunting wall of dark lances. Before the sweetness of the honey can be tasted, one must bear a sting as piercing as the wounds of arrows. How many people of noble birth wander in this sacred retreat! They endure with patience the bitter trials attached to their sublime passion. They fast and they spend dark nights in humble prayers. The violence of desire annihilates their spirit, their bodies consumed by an ardour that burns. But alas! Divine love still sees nothing but a terrible void in their hearts. The home of the good, who have fully overcome their passions, is pointless to yearn for, if you cannot conquer your own.

ALLEGORY XXV
The Bee

What pretentiousness!—the bee at once exclaimed. What the duck has said of his travels is untrue, that bird is deluded indeed! How different is the truly religious man; his merit is apparent, he has no need to brag; his inner purity shows forth in his most secret actions. For sure, whoever does not succumb to conceit, whatever his worth to warrant it, adds yet the greatest value to his excellence. So do not ever say a word that your actions belie nor bring up a son that your race would disown! Learn to love light, wholesome foods and pure, natural liquids. See how my dignity finds dimension and my merit perfection when I am able to gather the fairest of food and quench my thirst in clear water.

Would God have deigned to inspire me had I not fed on the right nutrition; had I not become enamoured of the noblest traits, walking with humility in the way of the Lord, like God's friends, and thanking him for his blessings?

I make my hive in the hills. I eat what can be gleaned from the trees without harming them, I eat what can be taken without the tiniest qualm. No architect could copy the construction of my comb. Euclid himself would profess admiration for the symmetry of my six-sided cells. I alight on flowers, I alight on fruits; and without spoiling the one or eating from the other, I draw out only a substance as light as the dew; content with this modest prize, I return then to my hive. There, leaving my work, I devote myself to my reflections and, in my prayers, I ceaselessly offer to God the tribute of my gratitude.

Urged by divine inspiration, I surrender myself in my works to the grace it is intended I attain. My wax and my honey are the product of both my knowledge and my work. Wax is the result of my labours; honey forms the fruits of all that I have been taught. Wax illuminates, honey is a salve. Some people seek the light my wax bestows, others the salutary sweetness of my honey. Only once they have suffered the gall of my sting will I release to the first my desired light, and only after ferocious fight will I give my honey to the rest. If any should try to strip me of my treasures by force, I defend them stoically from attack, should the price even be my life, and I say to myself, Take courage, O my soul! Then to him who tries to oust me from the garden that is my home, I say these words: Why come to torment me, O servant of hell!

If it is allegories you seek, there is one of value to be found in my condition. Reflect on this: you can only gain my favours by submitting with patience to the suffering from my sting.

VERSES

Bear patiently the gall of my disdain, you who wish to be one with me; think only of my love and leave him alone who foolishly struggles to keep us apart, daring to jeer at your pain. To live the spiritual life that you say you desire, you must be able to die before your appointed hour. How hard and narrow is the path of love! To embark on it we must sever all the ties that bind us to the world. But these pains that seem so bitter are all too sweet and love lightens the heaviest load.

If you aspire to reach the goal we aim for, learn to read the allegories offered you. And if you understand, advance. If not, stay in your place.

ALLEGORY XXVI
The Candle

The candle, at prey to the pain of devouring flames, shed copious tears and poured forth plaintive cries. Touched by compassion at the sound of her grief, the bee gave full ear as the candle spoke these words to her:

Why, by the cruelty of my fate, am I ever to be parted from you; you who are my mother, since my life comes from you, you are my cause, since I am your effect?

Alas, we were torn from your hive by fire, I, the wax, and the honey, my brother and companion. He shared with me your sanctuary; then the flame came to drive us out and, destroying the alliance that kept us close, put a great chasm beween us. But as if this cruel separation were not enough, I am again vulnerable to the violence of fire;and, although I am innocent, my heart is burned and my body made a slave.

Lovers grow intimate by the light I give, as I dwindle towards my destruction. The people of inner knowledge, by my illumination, engage in their meditations. To spread my light, to burn, to shed tears, for this it is I am destined. Ever ready to serve and bow, in patience, to both hardship and pain, I burn up myself to bless others with light, I take torment so that they take whatever of value is mine. How then could anyone with reason reproach my pallor and my tears?

And that is not all. Clouds of moths jostle to put out my flame and dim my very brilliance. In my anger I burn them as just desert for their daring. For it is known that evil befalls the doer and, even if moths were to swarm the earth, I still should not fear them. Just as, if the world were overrun with impious people, they would not be able to dim the torch of faith. Their blaspheming mouths try to blow out this sacred light but the Most Merciful would never permit it. This is an enigma whose meaning will be manifest to the one who knows how to decipher it.

VERSES

Light of my life, what brightness have I not received from you? Whether I take the true path or whether I stray, all comes from your blessed and adored hand. No critic could accuse me of falsity to you; no wind could extinguish the divine light with which you illuminate me.

ALLEGORY XXVII
The Moth

And then the moth, half-consumed by the flame, floundering and reeling on the carpet, complained bitterly to the candle in this way:

How can it be that at the moment when I surrender my heart to your love, directing my prayers to you alone, you cast me out as an enemy?

Who gave you the right to take my life? Who has incited you to inflict death on me, your single-hearted lover, your tenderest friend?

With patience I suffer the heat of your flame; alone of your lovers I dare to brave sure death. But tell me, have you ever known a mistress enjoy taunting her friend, or a doctor who works to make worse the suffering of his patient? What! I love you, yet you do me harm.

I come near you, and you scorch me with your blazing rays. Yet, far from defeating my love for you, your harshness serves only to increase it. I rush towards you, wretched thing that I am, overcome by my desire for us to consummate our union; but you reject me with cruelty and tear the gauze of my wings. No lover has ever experienced such a trial; never has anyone endured what I endure. And yet, despite all that I suffer, it is you alone I love, you alone that I adore. Do I not bear hardships enough already without your adding undeserved reproach?

VERSES

I came to my beloved to grieve of the torments of my heart but, instead of her allaying them, I am flung far with beating. In this way the moth pleads for union with his friend but the answer is to envelop him in devouring flames; he falls near the cruel one, overwhelmed by the ravages of fire, and deep he plunges into the abyss of sorrow. I promised myself the joy of an instant of bliss, but I did not think of the bitter pains of love. To be devoured by desire, consumed by ardour, that is the law to which lovers must submit.

*   *   *

When the moth had explained the cause of his suffering, in plaint of his afflictions and pains, compassion moved the candle, who spoke to him thus:

True lover, do not be too hasty to condemn me. For I endure the same torments as you, the very same pains and hardships. Listen to this most extraordinary of tales and have pity for the most violent suffering. It is not unusual for a lover to be consumed; but for a loved one to share that fate is truly strange. That fire loves me and his impassioned sighs burn and melt me; in his wish to draw near me, he devours me. He aspires to my love and wishes to be one with me, yet, once he has fulfilled his desires, he can only exist by destroying me. Surely it is strange that a mistress should perish while her lover survives her! That her lover should have joy while his beloved has grief.

The fire then answered: O you who stand bewildered in the glow of my rays, tormented by my flame, why complain when the sweet moment of union is yours to enjoy? Happy he who drinks, with me as his cupbearer, happy his life who, consumed by my immortal flames, dies to himself to obey the laws of love!

VERSES

As the night laid its mournful veil on the earth, I said to the candle that gave me light: My heart is easily moved by the fate of my friends and when I see others shedding tears, I cannot help but weep myself.

Before pointing the finger at my sorrow, she said, listen in full to my story. If blind fortune has made you familiar with sadness, know that from me she has taken a brother, a brother endowed with health-giving balm and a sweet, untarnished flavour. Your eyes are moist with tears at the thought of the beauty whose lips are as soft and whose breath is honeyed. I am aware of your sorrow. Why will you not allow me mine, the affliction of the loss of my brother? Would I not be more worthy of blame if I withheld my tears? Fire has parted me from this cherished brother: and by fire I have sworn to end my life.

ALLEGORY XXVIII
The Crow

I was still listening to the candle's words, surrendering to the fancies they brought to mind, when I heard the lugubrious caw of the crow. Together with his friends, he is the omen of fatal separation. Dressed in mourning and, alone among men, clothed in black, he moaned as one who suffers misfortune and bewailed the cruelty of his pain. O, one who ceaselessly laments, I said, your untimely cries come to taint what is purest and turn bitter what is most sweet! Why, from early morning, do you incessantly speak of separation, these springtime camps the target for your tirade? If you see perfect happiness, you forecast its imminent end; if you see a fine castle, you say that its place will soon be taken by ruins. You are a worse omen than Qashir for those who enjoy the pleasures of life and more sinister than Jadhir for the prudent, reflective man.

In his own defence, the crow then adopted the eloquent language expressive of his station in life:

Hapless man, he said to me, you cannot distinguish good from evil; your enemy and your friend are equal in your eyes! You understand neither allegory nor reality; the advice you are given is like so much wind in your ears! And the words of the sage have as much rein on your emotionality as the barking of a dog. And so you give no thought to your approaching departure from the vast playground of the earth for the shadows of the grave and the narrow confines of the tomb. You are heedless of the accident which brought to the father of men such burning regrets; of Noah's prophecy of the place where rest is no man's; of the fate of Abraham, the friend of God, encircled by the flames into which Nimrod cast him. Do you not know how to learn from the patience of Ishmael, on being sacrificed by his father? Or the repentance of David who so grievously regretted his crime? The exemplary piety and self-denial of Jesus the Messiah? Do you refuse to see that the most perfect of happiness has its term and that even the very purest rapture fades? That peace is broken and sweetness turns sour? Where is the hope that death does not destroy, the caution not made meaningless by destiny? Is the messenger of happiness not followed closely by the herald of misfortune? What is easy, does it not become difficult? Where is there anything that is immutable? Where is the man who passes not away? Where is the fortune that stays in its owner's hand? And what has become of that long-lived man who was the object of awe in his lifetime, or that happy mortal who was drenched in riches, or that beauty whose complexion was textured like lilies and roses?

Does death not come to claim men, one after another, and

take them from among the living? Are not the base slave and the glorious master reduced to the same dust? Has divine inspiration not suffused in the sensualist, cradled in the bosom of plenty, these words from the Koran, where God said to the Prophet: "Tell that enjoyment of this world is of little consequence in the next!" Why then speak ill of my moans and take as ominous my plaintive cawing, whether at break of day or the onset of night? If you knew your true happiness as I know mine, you would not wait to don black garb, as I have, and you would answer me with lamentations of your own: but pleasure takes up your every moment; your vanity and self-love hold you back.

As for myself, I give warning to the traveller that wherever he stops, those places will soon be destroyed. I caution the careless eater about the harmful foods of the world and I tell the pilgrim that he is approaching the end. Your true friend is the one who talks to you frankly, not the one who hangs on to your every word; the one who reprimands you, not the one who excuses you; the one who teaches the truth, not he who avenges your injuries; for whoever remonstrates with you is awakening within you virtue when it has slipped into sleep. He who fills you with healthy fears is keeping you on your guard. For my part, I have tried to imprint these same things in your mind by my dark coloured wings and my warning call. I have even made you hear my cry in the midst of your making merry. But one could apply this proverb to me! You talk to a dead man.

VERSES

I cry for the fugitive life which escapes me and I have good reason to voice my complaints aloud. I cannot help myself from crying out each time I see a caravan urged on by its driver. Unthinking people criticise me for my mourning clothes but I say to them: I am a symbol of the very thing I teach; I am like the Khatib, the preacher, who is always dressed in black. At the first sight of a springtime encampment you will see me announce in every valley its imminent departure for another place, and then bemoan its fading traces, in plaint of a cruel absence. But only dumb, inanimate objects answer my voice. O you, hard of hearing, wake up at last and learn the lesson of the morning cloud; there is no one on earth who is spared the duty to try to glean something of the invisible world. Remember that all men are called, sooner or later. I would have been heard, if I had said these words to one living being. But alas. I speak to a dead man!

ALLEGORY XXIX
The Hoopoe

Once the crow had thus marred my moments of happiness in that garden and urged me to be on my guard against attracting hatred to myself, I stopped being absorbed by the smiling beauty that surrounded me and returned to the solitude of my thoughts. Falling into a dream, I felt myself as if inspired and seemed to hear clearly the following words:

You who listen to the silent language of the birds and complain that happiness seems to elude you, be sure that if the heart is inclined to learn, the mind will penetrate the meaning of the allegories! Then the pilgrim of this world would remain on the path and the one whom pleasures bedazzle would not stray. If the spirit were good, it would perceive the signs of truth; if conscience were capable of understanding, it would learn the glad news without struggle; if the soul opened itself to mystical influence, it would attain higher understanding; if it were known how to draw aside the veil, what is hidden would be revealed; if the life were pure, the mysteries of the invisible would become apparent and the divine mistress would let herself be looked upon. If you kept yourself apart from the things of this world, the door of spirituality would open to you. If you shed your garment of self-love, nothing else would constrict you. If you avoided the world of error, you would perceive the spiritual realm. If you cut the ties which bind you to the pleasures of the senses, certain truths would be clear to you; and if you reformed your ways, you would no longer be deprived of divine food.

If you overcame your desires, you would attain the fullness of the contemplative life; if you conquered your emotions, God would draw you nearer to Himself. He would unite you with Himself if, to please him, you sacrificed the bond to your father and if you renounced yourself, you would find near the divinity the sweetest home.

However, far from that, you are a captive in the prison of your inclinations, chained to your habits, enslaved by desires and deluded by your senses; you are held back by your cold determination, consumed by the fire of greed and weighed down by an overload of senseless joy. A deadly languor blinds you, your blood is aroused by the impulses of unruly love, your weak will takes only half-hearted resolutions and abandons itself only to brittle thoughts.

Your corrupted spirit forces you into a state of painful hesitation and, in your perverse judgment, you see good as evil and evil as good.

Your aim should be to enter the hospice of piety, to present there the cup of your affliction and speak all your sufferings to that physician who knows what is concealed as well as what is revealed. In your burning thirst, you would hold out your wrist for him to take the pulse of your malady and to examine the nature of your fever. Then, having diagnosed fully your unhappy predicament, he would pass you over to the person whose task it is to mete out the punishments of the law. And he would bind you with the bonds of fear and strike you with the rods of indecision and hesitation, yet at the same time reviving you with the fan of hope. Then he would have you stay in the sanctuary of protection and note down in his casebook the course of your convalescence. For you he would prepare potions of the myrobalan of refuge, the violet of hope, the scammony of confidence, the tamarind of direction, the jujube of solicitude, the sebesten of correction, the plum of sincerity and the cassia of free will. He would crush them all on the surface of acceptance, pound the mixture in the mortar of patience, sieve it in the riddle of humility and purify it by the sugar of graceful action. And then, after the night-time vigil, he would give you this medicine in the calm of morning, attended by the spiritual physician, closeted with the divine friend and unknown to the jealous rival, to see if your agitation would be appeased, your heated passions cool, your heart, lost to you by heedless living, would return to its place—and your temperament keep the balance that is spiritual health. If only your ear could learn the language of the mystery, and hear these gentle words! Has someone made a request? I am ready to grant it. This way will I know if your inner sight is striving for illumination, if you have the capacity for contemplation of the spiritual world's many marvellous and extraordinary things.

Think of the hoopoe. When her actions are right and her heart is pure, her sight can penetrate to the core of the earth and find there what is hidden from others' eyes. She sees the water that runs there as you might see it through crystal. And, guided by her certainty and sensitive taste, she says:

Here the water is sweet, while there the water is bitter. I dare make the claim that, in my tiny body, I possess that which Solomon never possessed, Solomon to whom God gave an unparalleled kingdom. I wish to talk of the skill God has given me, a skill with which not even Solomon, nor any of his kin, were endowed. Everywhere I attended that mighty monarch, kept near him whatever his pace. And I showed him the places where water was under the ground. Then one day, unexpectedly, I disappeared and, in my absence, he lost his power. He then said to his courtiers and the members of his suite:

I do not see the hoopoe. Has she abandoned me? If she has, I shall make her suffer a sad punishment, I may even offer her in sacrifice as my vengeance, if she can give no good reason for her act.

It is remarkable, is it not, that he noticed me only when I was not there to help? Wishing to make the power of his authority felt, he railed on in this same vein: I will punish her, no, I'll kill her.

But destiny said: I will send her to you, I will bring her myself. And when from Sheba I returned, entrusted with a message for the mighty king, I said to him: I know what you do not. But this only made worse his anger against me and he cried out these words:

You whose tiny body is yet filled with such malice, not content to rouse my anger by leaving my presence, you now pretend that you are wiser than I!

Mercy, O Solomon, I said to him. I concede you sought an

empire unequalled ever by those of other sovereigns but *you* must admit that you did not also ask for a wisdom the like of none other. I have brought from Sheba news that all the wise men ignore.

O hoopoe, he then said, those who know how to carry themselves with prudence can be trusted with the secrets of kings. Take then my letter.

I made haste to do this and to bring back an answer. And then it was that he showered me with favours. He made me one of his friends and I took my place among the guardians of the curtain at his door, whereas once I had not dared approach it. To honour me he then put a crown on my head, an ornament that does much to ennoble me. After this, all thought of slaying me was forgotten and verses in my praise were sung instead. As for you, if you are able to take this advice, correct your conduct, purify your conscience, restore your true nature, feel fear for the one who has brought you from nothingness and learn from the valuable lessons he gives, even when it is through animals that he does so. And know this. The man who fails to extract the significance from the sharp creak of the door, the buzzing of the bee, the barking of the dogs, the industry of the insects in the dust; he who knows not what is signified by the motion of the cloud, the shimmer of the mirage and the shading of the mist, this man does not number among the perceptive ones of the essence.

VERSES

You are sweeter to my senses than the breath of the zephyr that ripples through the gardens at night. The merest thought of you sets me astir and troubles me. Everything of beauty is like a cup in which I see your much-loved face; in every sound it seems I hear your beloved voice.

ALLEGORY XXX
The Dog

Absorbed by the charm of the birds' discourse, I was waiting to hear their answer to the hoopoe when a dog by the door, scratching out crumbs of bread from the rubbish, spoke to me in these words:

You, who have not yet lifted the veil of the mystery, you are bedazzled by the things of this world and cannot rise to the level of your primeval origins! You, pompously dragged down by the heavy garment of self-love, copy my noble actions, acquire my good qualities and, without recoiling at my low status, listen to what I will tell you of my wise behaviour. Seen from your posture, I can be only an object of contempt. But, if you care to look closely, you will see instead that I am a true fakir, a humble one. Ever at the door of my masters, I do not seek a more distinguished place; ever among men, I do not change my mode of being. I am chased out, yes, but I come back. I am beaten but I never bear a grudge. My friendship is firm and my fidelity beyond question.

I watch while men sleep and I keep a careful guard when meals are served. Yet I am awarded no pay, no food, nor even shelter, much less a distinguished place. I show gratitude when given, patience when pushed away. Nowhere am I ever to be seen complaining or crying of the harsh way I am handled. When I am sick, no one visits me, when I die, I have no coffin. If I leave one place to go to another, no one gives me food. I have no money to be passed on, no fields that can be ploughed. When I am absent, no one wills my return, even children are not sad for me. No one sheds a tear. And when I am found, no one bothers to notice me. Meanwhile I keep up my guard around men's homes and always remain faithful. Forced to feed from the rubbish outside their doors, I am grateful simply for what I have got, deprived of the favours that should be showered on me. If you find my ways pleasing, follow my example, match your actions to mine and, if you want to be like me, take my life as the model for your own.

VERSES

Learn from me how to carry out the duties of friendship and by following my way, raise yourself up to the noblest virtue Wretched, despised animal I may be, but my heart is free o vices. My way is to guard those who dwell in the quarter wher I live, and especially I protect them at night. Always patien and even grateful, no matter my condition, I never complain o man's injustice and content myself with trusting in God alone Regardless of these virtues, no one pays me any notice, whethe cruel hunger kill me or misfortune feed me from a bitter cup o pain and sorrow. Yet I choose to endure the bad treatment tha befalls me, in preference to losing my self-respect and degrad ing myself to beg. Yes, I fear not to say this: spurned though am, I have more to commend me than other animals.

ALLEGORY XXXI
The Camel

The camel spoke:
You who wish to take the road to the palace of the king, tak your lessons in abstinence and poverty from the dog, but lear of constancy and patience from me! For, whoever freely make the choice of poverty, patience, too, he must strive to acquire. A poor man gifted with this virtue should be counted as one of th rich.

I complete the longest journeys, laden with heavy burdens. brave the dangers of the desert and suffer the harshes handling, without ever losing heart. When I walk, I do not rus senselessly ahead but I, who could stave off the sturdiest mar let myself be led even by a child. My disposition being obedien and gentle, I bear baggage and loads on both sides of me. I ar not treacherous nor easily disheartened. I do not becom presumptuous when I overcome obstacles and difficulties d not make me turn back. I make boldly for the muddy, slipper roads where the most intrepid other travellers would fear to tread. With fortitude I bear the burning thirst of the south and never do I stray from that path that is marked for me. At the end of the journey, with my duty towards my master fulfilled, I throw the halter off my back and make for the fields.

I take for my food what is there for the picking and can be eaten without any qualm. But if suddenly I hear the voice of my driver, I give him my bridle, and, foregoing the pleasure of sleep, I stretch out my neck, as if the sooner to reach my journey's end. If I err, my driver directs me; if I stumble, he comes to my aid; if I am thirsty, the name of my beloved serves as my water and food. I am destined for the service of man, as in that passage where it is said: "He carries your loads." And I never stop my steps till I reach the place which is the end of all life's pilgrimage.

VERSES

O Saad! If you come this way, question a heart that has penetrated the inviolable sanctuary where dwells this ravishing being. And if, in the distance, your eyes light on this sandy mound, remember that impassioned lover, troubled and torn by the tenderest love.

Camels, when we come within sight of Medina, let us stop. Never again leave this sacred enclosure. But what is this? When the valley of Al-Aqiq appears before them, they all move on, swaggering with an ostrich-strutting stride.

Brother, shed with me tears of desire for the beauty whose ravishing face puts even the full moon to shame; and when your time comes in that blessed garden, do not fail to say: Dweller of the tribe, I salute you.

ALLEGORY XXXII
The Horse

Lessons learned from the dog have made you a fakir, lessons

learned from the camel have given you patience. If you would
seek out the path that leads to acts of glory, said the horse, I will
teach you, in my turn, the nature of eminence and how to make
real use of efforts to gain success. Even with a rider on my back
who plies me with abuse, see how, with the speed of a bird on
the wing, I spring forth in my flight; like the night when it
spreads its dark veil across the earth, or like a rushing torrent.

If my rider is on the chase, with me to aid him he will easily
reach the object of his desire. But if, on the contrary, he is being
pursued, I keep him ahead and my swift gallop draws him away
from his foe, who—barely touching the dust thrown up by my
feet—soon loses me from sight and has to rely on others to tell
him where I have gone.

If it is proven that the camel is patient, my gratitude for
kindness is also well known.

The camel reaches truth at the goal he has set himself; but, as
for me, I am ever the front line in the war against the infidel. On
the day of battle, at the moment of attack, I spring boldly
forward like one who knows no fear, ahead of the hail of his
deadly arrows.

But the camel stays back, to be laden with heavy goods, or to
have its baggage unpacked. The charge that I have can only be
met by those who are able to keep their pledges; only those
whose step is light and swift can take the road assigned to me.
So I train myself for agility and get myself ready for the
reckoning day. When I see a man whose own foolish heedless-
ness has sunk him in a drunken stupor, his recovery hopeless
and he is completely distracted by the pleasures of life, I say to
him:

Nothing you possess is other than ephemeral; only God's
gifts are eternal. O you, who have been driven so far off from
what you desire so ardently; you, set aside from that mysterious
combat, look deep into nature and try to understand the
Creator's purpose. Then at once set yourself a strict code to live
by and set a short rein on your senses. Remember, fate has
decreed the moment of your death, the number of your breaths
is charted by destiny. Fear the coming of the terrible judgment
day.

As for me, when the groom has put me in my harness, those
who mount me have nothing to fear from my mettle. Have they

not often dined on the spoils of the hunt, their victory owed to my speed? I always leave behind whoever tries to pass me and I always pass whoever I am pursuing. I am haltered to stop me from setting about other horses; I am guided with reins so that I may not stray from the road I am called upon to follow; I am fitted with a bridle to keep my neck and shoulders elegantly upright; my rein is shortened for fear that I may forget to hold myself erect; and my feet are shod to prevent me tiring when I spring into action on the racing-ground.

The Supreme Being, unequalled in beneficence, has showered me with his bounty and has judged in my favour in his eternal goodness. Until the day of Resurrection happiness is bound to the tuft of hair that adorns the forehead of horses. As son of the wind, I have been inspired to bless and praise God. To whomever mounts me, my back bestows a glory of its own. My flank is a treasure for any owner and to have my friendship means good fortune. How often have I been goaded on into the arena without my showing any weakness! How often, after taking first prize for my speed in the race, have I not been swathed in silk, the stuff of infidels! So many times, too, have I triumphed over hypocrites and swept them from the surface of the earth! Do they have any power now, do you still hear of them?

VERSES

Come forward with a light swift step; you will find a happiness all the more precious for the trials that precede union with this beloved. Generous lovers, walk with courage in the steps of the Prophet, ennobled by sanctity in its most pure form. Those who, in their progress along the mystical path, have climbed to the heights of spirituality, they are blessed with a sight of this ravishing view that shines with the brightest radiance. It is perhaps for you, too, to join these fortunate ones who, from the dawn of existence, have tasted these sweet moments of ecstasy!

*   *   *

Yes, I then said to the horse, you do indeed have the finest of qualities and your actions are worthy of praise.

ALLEGORY XXXIII
The Lynx

I was lost in thought when the lynx spoke these words to me:

Wise witness of nature, learn from me about pride and right manners. Led by the loftiness of my aspirations and the boldness of my designs, I take heed of everything that can bring me closer to the object of my love. And I end by taking my seat at the side of my beloved. When I pursue my prey, I am not as swift as the horse; and when I reach it, I do not fell it in the way of the lion; I try to deceive by cunning and guile the animal it is in my sights to slay; but if I do not at once succeed, my violent anger flares. Others of my kin try to calm me down but it is not my will to listen, insensitive to right manners and kindness.

My emotion is the stuff of my weakness and impotence. Yes, whoever would be perfect but lacks the strength, whoever wants virtue but his soul will not comply, he must—I repeat, must—let the anger of conceit burst only against himself; he must take heart anew, redouble his efforts and eschew, if he is to succeed, a weakened will and poorly thought-out plans.

There is something else of value to be learned from my life but it only has meaning for the mind that can make sense of allegory; my greed adds excess to my blood and my flesh and makes me inordinately fat. Weighed down by this superabundance of bulk, I fear being caught if I am pursued; I fear defeat in the arena, if attacked. Then you will see me run from my own kind and hide at the back of my lair, there to grapple with my conscience. As corrective steps, I hold off from my habits, restraining my nature; I mortify my heart with abstinence, the basis of devotion. And when my thoughts soar and my ardour is true, my body purified of corruption, and languor banished from my soul, then I go forth from my solitary hiding-place. My infirmities gone, no longer am I fearful wherever I live and I settle in which place I please. If you think you can copy me, travel this ground and, like me, break out of old habits for ever.

VERSES

I saw the lynx fly into violent passion when he pounced on his prey but could not bring it to ground; so must it be for the wise and generous man who walks on the path; if gentle joy of spirit, so hard to acquire, is ever to be his.

ALLEGORY XXXIV
The Silkworm

Athletic movements or abstention from refreshment are not the qualities that make a man nor, said the silkworm, is there any merit in giving away things which are made to be given away. True generosity is that which teaches the liberal giving of one's own necessities, the giving of one's very life. So, when it comes to the count, the most valuable of qualities are found among simple worms. I am but one of this many-formed species and I tend to draw close to those who show me affection.

In essence but a grain, I am gathered like the seed to be sown in the earth; sometimes men, sometimes women, keep me warm in their bosom and when this life-giving nurture has reached its term, my birth permitted by Divine Power, I emerge from this grain and show myself to the light. On the day of my birth I look at myself and see I am nothing but a helpless orphan; but man lashes me with attention, saves me from any hurtful foods and gives me always the right nutrition. My education over, I start to gain in strength and vigour and make haste to do for my benefactor what gratitude demands and return what I owe to those who have treated me well. And so I start work that is useful to man, in keeping with the words, 'Can the reward of a favour be other than a favour?'

Without pride or complaint at the hard work I set myself,

inspired by my destiny, I weave from my silken liquor a thread matchless even by those gifted with the greatest skills. For this, gratitude extends to me after my death. This thread is used to make materials which enrich those that wear them and add refinement even to the very staid. Kings themselves are proud to wear cloth woven from my cocoon and emperors seek clothes of my shining silk. Silk decorates playfellows, and gives new allure to youthful beauties whose breasts are beginning to round. All in all, it is the most sensual, the most elegant of attire.

When I have done for my benefactor what gratitude demands of me, complying thus with the rule of reciprocity, I make my tomb from the house I have woven, for within this cocoon must my resurrection take place. My work is to narrow the walls of my prison and, willing my death, I bury myself between them. Thinking only of the good of others, I give with generosity all I possess, keeping for myself only sorrow and trouble. Exposed, as I am, to the sorrows of this world, whose very foundations are unhappiness and misfortune, I am made to suffer a scorching fire and the jealousy of the neighbouring spider, unjust and unkind to me.

This spider, as it works its weaving of the most fragile of homes, not content with worry caused me by its irksome proximity, dares also to compete with me. He says: My weaving is like yours, our work has the same flaws and you and I suffer the same burning fire; it is in vain you pretend to be my superior. For shame, say I in my turn, your web is a net to trap flies and hold dust, whereas what I weave will adorn the most high-born of princes. And are you not the spider whose weakness is written in the Koran for all eternity? Has your weakness not now become proverbial? Yes, I can say it, the difference between you and me is the difference between antimony's artefact eye-shadow black and the natural blackness of the eye; as different as a full moon and a setting star.

VERSES

The secret of my spun silk liquor I owe to him that guides us

o the path of virtue and bestows on us our fortune. You who
wish to imitate my work, do you really imagine that from your
coarse cloth could come the rich raiment made from my
precious thread? Can one, without falsehood, claim merit for
oneself when one cannot be useful to others?

ALLEGORY XXXV
The Spider

You may suppose, said the spider, that my home is so fragile
that I am worth naught but contempt; yet my superiority is
recorded in the book of time. No one can say in reproach that
care is lavished on me; nor have maternal tenderness and
paternal kindness ever been mine to enjoy. From the moment of
my birth, I settle myself in a corner of the house and start to
weave.

I like a hovel best, and my affinity is for angles, because there
one can hide and find a mass of mysterious things.

When I find a place where I can easily cast my net, I toss my
sticky liquor first on one wall then the other, careful not to
entangle the threads of my web. Then, through the pores of my
spinneret, I secrete a slender thread that floats down through
the air. And, suspended from it, upside down, I let hang limp
those claws that serve me as hands. Thus anyone, deceived by
this position, could truly take me for dead.

If the fly passes now, I trap it in the web spun out by my
cunning and I imprison it in my hunting-snare. I know you
have an honour of which I am deprived; as I cannot, like you,
weave precious stuff to grace this transitory abode. But where
were you on the Night of the Cavern, when I, with my
protective web, hid the Prophet, the Chosen, keeping him from
view and delivering him from the legions of the miscreants? I
did for him then what the fugitives (from Mecca) and the
helpers (of Medina) could never, ever have done. In the same
way I guarded the ancient and revered Abu Bakr, who came

with him to Medina and the cavern and who followed him out
in the road of honour and glory. As for you, you use your
frivolous cloth only to deceive and seduce; and your handiwork,
destined to drape women with empty minds and to be a
diversion for unreasoning children, is forbidden to men, for its
lustre cannot last, its use has no value and it confers no benefit
for the Path. Alas!

How sad the man who is shunned by his mistress and from
whom she takes all hope of her ever being his; whom she
deprives of her favours, denying him even the pleasure of
asking; whom pitilessly she expels from her presence, forbid-
ding him to approach!

VERSES

O you who delight in sumptuous splendour and magnificent
chambers, you must have forgot that this world is but a place
for standing devotion. After sleeping on these luxurious beds,
tomorrow you will descend to the narrow dark cell of the tomb.
Your companions will be silent beings, but the energy in their
silence is akin to speech. Ah, that a simple dress should be all
your clothing and a spoonful or two should be all your food!
Choose, like the spider, a modest dwelling and say to yourself:
let us stay here and wait for death.

ALLEGORY XXXVI
The Ant

If a hostile fate lets fly its darts at you, confront it with stoic
calm, said the ant. And when you see someone ready to take the
spiritual path, set out before, and do not foolishly forget to take
right action in that life. Take a lesson from me and see the
importance of preparations and building up provisions for your
future life. Look at the lofty goal that is constantly in my sight

and see how the hand of Providence has acted to gird my loins, like a slave, to save me from having to tighten, then loosen, my belt. When I emerge from non-being, opening my eyes, you can see me hastening to join the servants. With the benign assistance for my guide, I then turn to the collection of necessary provisions; and here I have advantage over even the most intelligent man, for my ability to scent extends to a considerable distance.

Back in my cell, I tidy the grains I have gathered for my food. He who makes the almond and fruits with stones to be opened inspires me to cut each grain in two equal halves; except for the seed of the coriander which, instinctively, I cut in four. This extra care is needed to stop it from germinating later. For, cut in two, it would not stop reproducing.

In the winter, when I fear that the soil's humidity may spoil my grains, I expose them to the air on a day when the sun is out, so that its heat may dry them. And so I go on. But you pretend that these measures are misguided, that they bode ill for me and that all this shows too much attachment to the goods of this world! You are wrong, I assure you.

If you knew what makes me act in this way, you would excuse me yourself and hold me in higher regard than you do now. Know that God (His is the Glory and Dignity) has armies unknown: except to him, as Exalted God has said: "No one knows the armies of your Lord, save He." But under the ground there is an army of ants, whose numbers can be counted only by God. We observe the rules of service to God, we are not attached other than to Him. We trust only in Him and our attention is on Him alone. And so from our midst he raises up those whom He wishes to set above us and he asks our submission, so our leaders may promise us blessings. These promises heard, unhesitating we go forth, without opposing. And on our departure, you could say of us thus:

VERSES

O my beloved, upon you the Peace of Allah, my farewells

spoken with tears of pain in my eyes, at the thought of separation. We shall live, I hope, and God will crown our love; but if death should strike us, we will find ourselves together in a happier life.

*   *   *

We make all our efforts, constantly collecting, to be useful to others than ourselves. But, prey to a thousand kinds of death, some of us perish from hunger or thirst, others fall into crevices of rocks from which they cannot escape; here a fly snaps them, there a four-footed creature or some other animal tramples them underfoot; should they escape these, there is yet a bird to make of them a meal. Some from amongst us die in sanctity, others do not attain salvation.

In the end, in accordance with His speech (may He be Exalted!): "There are believers who have sincerely kept promises made to God", we put before us all we possess and we share it equally among ourselves, with no partiality or injustice.

If you are accepted among the elect, you will be converted through the word of the Koran; but if the wings of your will fall short of lofty heights, your destiny will be a dark one.

ALLEGORY XXXVII
The Anqa Bird

O you who can understand allegory, here is one which cannot fail to please you; if you think you can catch the hidden meaning of my story, listen hard to enigmatic hints which speak my secret.

It is related that one day the birds assembled and said to each other: We cannot manage without a king whom we recognise and who will accept us. So let us then look for one to whom we will be bound and, obedient to his law, we shall live in his protection, sheltered from all evil, as if shaded by a tree with lush leaves. We were told that in one of the islands out at sea lived a bird called Anqamaghrib, whose authority is accepted from East to West; be sure he is our king, let us fly to him.

But the sea is deep, the birds were told; the road is hard and immeasurably long; you have to scale high mountains, cross a stormy ocean and face devouring flames. Please take it on trust, you could not reach this mysterious island: and even if you were to triumph over all hardships, approach to the sacred one is stopped at the sharp point of the lance. Stay therefore in your nests, since weakness is your way and this mighty monarch has no need of your praise. As it says in the Koran: "God has no need of creatures." Destiny warns you to mistrust your ardour and God gives the self-same advice.

True enough, said the birds, but the desires of love focus our hearing on these words from the Koran: "Go towards God." And so they winged their way forth through the air, as alluded to in a passage from the book: "They think of the creation of heaven and earth." They endured with patience burning thirst in the south, according to those words: "He who leaves his house to escape." They went without ever winging from their way, since, if they took to the right, despair came to freeze them, if they took to the left, flames of fear came to burn them.

Sometimes they tried to pass each other, at other times they followed passively behind. They suffered the torments of the gloom of dark nights, of prostration, and flames and faintness of heart; they were tortured in turns by the angry seas, the remoteness of the place and their isolation. At last they all came to that very island for which they had abandoned their homeland; but one by one they came, not together, featherless and thin and dismal-hearted, those birds who had been so robust when they took wing.

When they entered the domain of the mighty king, they found there all that the soul can desire and all that the eyes can hope to see. Those who were attracted to the delicacies of the table heard these words from the Koran: "Help yourself to wholesome, light food as reward for the good you did in the other life." Those who liked fine clothes and dresses were told these words: "They will be dressed in costly cloth and watered-silk clothes and will be put before each other." For those who were drawn to the pleasures of love, "We have united them with the celestial houris."

But when those given to contemplation saw the nature of this distribution: What? they said. Will eating and drinking be our occupation, here as it was on earth? Will the lover be able to give himself over to the worship of his loved one? When will he gain the honour for which his wishes burn? No, whoever sells himself cheap does not deserve the least attention. As for ourselves, all we want is this king for whom we have crossed the stony deserts, triumphed over hardships and endured with patience the burning thirst of the south, ever in memory this passage: "He who leaves his house to escape." In any case, we have set little store by fine clothing and other earthly pleasures. No, once more, by him alone who is God, it is only him that we desire, him alone that we want for ourselves.

But then, why have you come, the king said to them, and what did you bring with you? They replied: Humility, which is fitting for your servants—and, indeed, you know better than we the thing that we desire.

Go back, he told them. Yes, I am king, whether you like it or not, and God has no need of you.

Lord, we know, they replied, that you do not need us; but not one of us can do without you. You are most excellent, whereas we are miserable and low; you are strong, we are weakness itself. How could we go back whence we came? Our strength is exhausted, our troop is indescribably depleted; and the crossings we have borne have destroyed our earthly bodies.

By my glory and dignity, then said the king, since your poverty is truly self-imposed and your humility certain, it is my duty to lift you from your miserable mire. Heal the one who is sick and, all of you, come to this fresh, shady garden, there to taste the most delightful rest.

If your hopes have grown cool, take a draught which is mixed with ginger; if, however, you have let yourself be led by the burning heat of desire, quench your thirst from a cup tinged with camphor. Tell this faithful lover who walked the spiritual path: Drink at the fountain named Salsabil. Bring the sick man to his doctor, since his fever of love is real; lead the lover to the side of his beloved, since his mystical death is complete.

Then the Lord suffused them with happiness and joy and made them drink a purifying liquor; and, as soon as they drank, they were overwhelmed by a wonderful intoxication. Later they danced to melodious music; they desired some new pleasure and the desire was fulfilled; they made various requests and these were granted. In the presence of Gabriel, they took to flight on the wings of familiarity; and, eager to seize chaste love's unblemished seed, they went down into that most delightful place where dwelt the powerful king. On the instant of their arrival, happiness became theirs and, in their eager scanning of this sacred place, they saw that nothing now concealed the face of their adored one; that the cups were set; that the lovers were linked with their divine friend . . . They saw at last what no eyes have seen and they heard what no ears have heard.

VERSES

O my soul, soar at the wondrous news I can tell you; once again your beloved is receiving your homage and your vows. The tent, sanctuary of mystery, is open to faithful lovers. Breathe in with delight the heady perfumes exhaled by this sacred tribe. See the lightning, the teller of most tender union, shining at a distance in the clouds. You shall live the sweetest life, always at the side of your own beloved, always with the image of your heart's devotions and nothing ever will be able to part you. Tears of absence will no longer fill your eyes; no pressing barrier will ever again block you from this blessed threshold. No longer will any irksome veil hide from you these radiant features; your eyes, drunk with love, will look forever on the ravishing beauty of the loved one, of whom even a glimpse is so fervently desired by countless lovers and for whom so many hearts are heavy with love.

كتاب

كشف الاسرار

عن حكم الطيور والازهار

لكاتبه

كتابي اسمى كروض زهـر
بـين النداما للــغـم نافى
فى الحسن اوحد والخط مفرد
والحظ يعهد والـــم خـافى

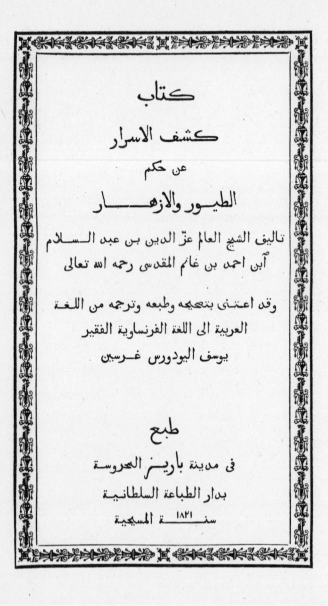

كتاب

كشف الاسرار

عن حكم

الطيــور والازهـــار

تاليف الشيخ العالم عزّ الدين بن عبد السـلام
ابن احمد بن غانم المقدسى رحمه الله تعالى

وقد اعتنى بتصحيحه وطبعه وترجمه من اللغـة
العربية الى اللغة الفرنساوية الفقير
يوسف البودورس غــرسين

طبع

فى مدينة باريـز المحروسة
بدار الطباعة السلطانية
سنــــــة ١٨٢١ المسيحية

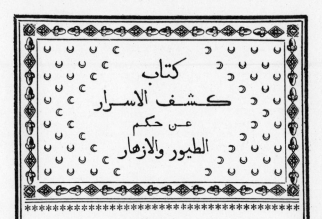

كتاب
كشف الاسرار
عن حكم
الطيور والازهار

بسم الله الرحمن الرحيم

الحمد لله القريب فى بعده، البعيد فى قربه،
المتعالى فى جَدّه، عن هزل القول وجِدّه، المقدس فى
رفيع مجده، عن حدّ وعدّه، الذى اوجد ما كان عدما،
واودع كل موجود حِكَمًا، وجعل العقل بينها حَكَمًا،
ليميّز بين الشىء وضده، والهمه بما عله فعلم مذاق
القول صافيه من شهده، فمن فكر بجميع قصده، ونظر
بتوفيق رشده، علم ان كل مخلوق فى قبضتَىْ شقائه
وسعده، مرزوق من خزائن نعمه ورفده، ما يفتح الله
للناس من رحمة فلا ممسك لها وما يمسك فلا مرسل

له من بعك، فلو صفت عين بصيرتك، وانجلت مراة
سريرتك، وامغين بسمع يقـظتـك، لاسمعك كـل
موجود ما يجك من فقدان وجك، وما يكابك مـن
وجدان فـقـك، الم تـرَ الى النسيم كيف تـنسم اسفـا
على بكا الحاب عن جزره ومك، وتاوه لهفا على نبسم
البرق لِـما سمع من قهقهة رعك، فانظـر الى الربيع
فها هو قد بشرك بورود ورده، واخبرك بشرود برده،
وسعى البك بانقلاب الشـتا بجردة ومـردة، وسـعى
البك بوشى الروض وبُرْده، وشكى البك البان مابان
من تمايل قك، وانهى البك الاقحوان ما كان مـن
الوان الزهر وجنك، وخفـوق اعلامه المعلة بسعك،
فوثب النرجس قائما للقيام بـورْده، واقبل الشقيق
على تـشـقيق ثوبه وقك، فكانه تـاكـل لاطم على
حمرة خك، وشكى البك للجلنار جل نار هجرة وصك،
وصاح العنـدليب على عودك، الرطيب برنك، وباح
العاشق الكئيب بما يكاتمه من هوى زينبه وهنك،
وهام فى فلوات خلوانه طربا بما سمعه عن طيب نجك،
وفر هربا الى من يعلم خفايا ما ابداه وما لم يبك،
فالعارف من شكر سوابغ النعم، واحتفر معادن

الحكم ، ولم يقنع من اللبن الا بزبده ، وعلم ان الله
ما احدث حدثًا، واهله عبثًا، بـل كل واقف عند
حده ، باق على حفظ ميثاقه وعهده ، مقر بـتصديق
وعده ووعده، وان من شىء الا يسبح بحمده، احمد واساله
توفيق حمده والهـام رشده ، واصلى واسلم علـى
رسوله الـذى انزل عليه فى محكم مجده، سبحان
الذى اسرى بعبده، فصلى الله عليه وعلى اصحابه واهل
بيته من بعده، وبعد فانى نظرت بعين التـحقيـق،
فرايت بنور التصديق والتوفيق، ان كل مخلوق مقر
بوجود الخالق، وكل صامت فى الحقيقة ناطق، فاستقريت
العبارات ، واستبريت الاشارات فرايـت كلا ناطقا
بلسان قاله، او بلسان حاله، لكنى رايت لسان الحال،
افصح من لسان القال، واصدق من كل مقال، لان لسان
الخبر يحتمل التكـذيب والتصديق ، ولسان العبر لا
ينطق الا بالتصديق والتحقيق، والناطق بلسان الحال،
مخاطب لذوى الاحوال ، والناطق بلسان القال، مقابل
لاهل العفة والاعتدال ، وقد وضعت كتابى هذا مترجما
عما استفدته من الحيوان برمزه، ومن الجماد بغمزه، وما
خاطبنى الازهار بلسان حالها، والتخارير عن مقرها

وارتحالها، وسميته كشف الاسرار عن حكم الطيور
والازهار، وجعلته موعظة لاهل الاعتبار، وتذكرة
لذوى الاستبصار، فاعتبروا يا اولى الابصار، فمن طالع
مقالى، وفهم ضرب امثالى، فذاك من امثالى، ومن اعجم
عليه اشكالى، فليس من اشكالى، ولقد اخرجنى الفكر
يوما لانظر ما احدثته ايدى القدم فى الحدث،
واوجدته للحكمة البالغة لا للعبث، فانتهيت الى
روضة قد رق اديمها، وراق نسيمها، ونم طيبها، وغنى
عندليبها، وتحركت عيدانها، وتمايلت اغصانها،
وتبلبلت بلابلها، وتسلسلت جداولها، وتسرحت
انهارها، وتصوغت اقطارها، وتفتقت ازهارها، وصوت
هزارها، فقلت يا لها من روضة ما اهناها، وخلوة ما
اصفاها، فيا ليتنى استصحبت صديقا حميما، يكون
لطيب حضرتى نديما، فنادانى لسان الحال، فى الحال،
اتريد نديما احسن منى، او مجيبا افصح منى، وليس
فى حضرتك شى الا وهو ناطق بلسان حاله، مناد
على نفسه بدنو ارتحاله، فاسمع له ان كنت من
رجاله،

شعر

الم ترَ ان نسيم الـصـبـا

له نفس نـشـره صاعـنُ

فطورا ينوح وطورا يـفـوح

كما يفعل الفاقد الـواجـنُ

وسكُب الغمام وندب الحمام

اذا ما شكى غصنه المـائـنُ

ونور الصباح ونـور الاقـاح

وقد هـزه البارق الـراعـنُ

ووافى الربيع بمعنى بـديـع

يـتـرجـمـه ورده الـوارنُ

وكل لاجلك مـسـتـنـبـط

لِمـا فيه نـفعك يا جاحنُ

وكـل لآيـه ذاكـر

مقرله شاكـر حامـنُ

وفى كـل شى لـه ايـة

تـدل عـلى انـه واحـنُ

nnnnnn

اثارة النسيم

فاول ما سمعت همهمة النسيم، بترنم بصوته الرخيم، يقول بلسان حاله، معفعا عن سقمه وانتحاله، انا رسول كل محب الى حبيبه، وحامل شكوى العليل الى طبيبه، وان استودعت سرا اديته كما استودعته، وان حُمّلت نشرا رويته كما سمعته، وان هببت معجوبا لاطفته بلطافة اناسي، ومازحته بصفا ايناسي، وان طاب طبت، وان خبث خبثت، ثم اني ان اعتللت مع بي العليل، وحيث حللت طاب بي المقيل، وان تنفست تنفس المشتاق، وان ترنمت توسوس العشاق، فانا لين الاعطاف، هين الانعطاف، سريع الايتلاف، يعترف بلطفي ذوى الالطاف، ولولا وجودى فى الجو لجان، ولاتظن ان اختلاف اهواى، سبب اغواى، بل اختلف فى الفصول الاربع، لما هو اصلح لك وانفع، فاهب فى الربيع شمالا فألقح الاشجار، واعدل فصل النبا والنهار،

واهب فى الصيف صبا فانمى الثمار، واصفى الاشجار،
واهب فى الخريف جنوبا فتاخذ كل ثمرة حد طيبها،
وتستوفى حق تركيبها، واهب فى الشتا دبورا لتخف
عن كل شجرة حملها، ويجف ورقها، ويبقى اصلها،
فانا الذى نمو بى الثمار، وتزهوا بى الازهار، وتسلسل
بى الانهار، وتلقح الاشجار، وتروح الاسرار، وابشر الزوار،
بقرب المزار،

شعر

يا طيب ما نـقـل النسيم لمسمعى

عن طيب ذاك المحـل الارفـــع

وافى لينشـر ما انطوى من نشره

فسكرت من طيب الشذا المتضوعى

ولربما اعتل النسيم اذا بــدت

انفاس وجدى المستكنّ باضلعى

هبّ الصبا سحرا لتبردّ غـــلّـتى

فاثار نار تحرقى وتـــوجّـــعـى

ما ذاك الا انـهـا لمـا سرت

مرت على تلك الــربى والاربعى

وتحملت عرف الشذا من طيبها

فسكرت حـــتى لا افيـق ولا اعى

وفهمت ما لم يفهم العشاق مـــن

سر الهوى وسمـــعـــت ما لم تسمعى

وافت تبشرنى بلــيــلى انــها

فى حسنها سفرت ولم تـتـبرقعى

وجلت على عشاقها فى حانـها

وجها تمنع فى حمى مـتـمـنـعى

~~~~~~~

اشاره الورد

ثم سمعت اشارة التفاريو بـافـنانها، والازاهيـر فى
تلون الوانها، اذ قام الورد يخبر عن طيب وروده،
ويعرف بعرفه عن شهوده، ويقول انا الضيف الوارد
بـين الشـتا والصيف، ازور زيارة الطيف، فاغتنموا
وقتى فالوقت سيف، اعطيت لون المعشوق والبست
ثوب العاشق، فاريج النــاشــق، واهيج المشوق الى
العاشق، فانا الزاير وانت المزور، والطمع فى بقاى
زور، ثم من علامة الدهر المكدور، والعـيـش
الممرور، اننى حيث ما نبت دايرُ الاشواك تزاحمنى،
وتجاورنى، فانا بين الادغال مطروح، وبنبال شـوكى
مجروح، وهذا دمى على ما عندى يلوح، فهذا حالى
وانا اشرف الوراد، والطف الاوراد، فمن ذا الذى
سلم من الانكاد، ومن صبر على مرارة الدنيا فقـد
بلغ المراد، فبيهما انا ارفل فى حلل النـضاره، اذ

اقتطفتنى ايدى النصارى ، فاسلمتنى من بين
الازاهير ، الى ضيق القوارير ، فيذاب جسدى ، ويحرق
كبدى ، ويهرق جلدى ، ويذهب جَلَدى ، ويقطر
دمعى الندى ، فلا يقام باودى ، ولا يوخذ بقودى ،
فجسدى فى حرق ، ودمعى فى غرق ، وكبدى فى قلق ،
وقد جعلت ما رشح من عرق ، شاهدا بما لقيت من
حرقى ، فيتاسى باحتراقى ، اهل الاحتراق ، ويتروح
بنفسى ذروا الاشواق ، فانا فارّ عنم باياى ، باق معم
بمعناى ، اهل المعرفة يتوقعون لقائُ ، واهل الحبة
يتمنون بقائُ ،

شعر

فان غبت جسما كنت بالروح حاضرا
فقربى سواء ان تاملت والـــبـــعـــد
وباه ما احظا من الناس قـــائـــلا
كانك ماء الورد اذ ذهـــب الورد

~~~~~~

اشارة المرسين

فلما سمع المرسين كلام الورد، قال قد لعب الغمام بالنرد، وباح النسيم بسرّه، ونشر السحاب عقود دره، وتضوع اليها بنخره، وتبهرج الربيع بقلائد فخره، وخلع الورد عذاره، وسحب عن الروض الانيق زهاره، وغرد الهزار، ولن للعاشق المزار، فقم بنا نتفرج، ونتنبه بحسننا ونتبهرج، فايام السرور تختلس، واوقاته باسرها تختبس، فلما سمع الورد كلام المرسين، قال له يا امير الرياحين، بئس ما قلت، ولو جمع بك الغضب ما صلت، فقد نزلت عن شيم الامرا، بعدم تاملك الصواب من الارا، فمن المصيب اذا زللت، ومن الهادى اذا ضللت، تامر باللهو عندك، وتحرض على النزه جندك، وامير الرعيه، صاحب الفكرة الرديه، فلا يعجبك حسنك، اذا تمايل غصنك، واخضر اوراقك، واكرم اعراقك، فايام

الشباب، كزيارة الاحباب، سريعة الزوال، دارسة
الطلال، كالطيف الطارق، والخيال المارق، يـطـرق
ويلمّ، فلا يقطع ولا يتمّ، وكذلك الشباب، اخضر
الجلباب والثياب، مختلف الاجناس، كاختلاف الحيوان
بين الناس، فنها ما يشم وينبل، ويحول خطابه
وينقل، وتطرقه حوادث الايام، ويعود مطروحا على
الاكوام، ومنها ما يوكل ثماره، وتجد فى الناس آثاره،
والسالم من النار اقله، ولولا القضا والقدر لسلم كله،
واياك واغترار، فى هذا الدار، فانما انت فريسة
لاسد الحمام، وبعد فقد نصحتك والسلام،

أشارة النرجس

فاجابه النرجس من خاطره ، وهو ناظر لمناظره ،
فقال انا رقيب القوم وشاهدهم ، وسميرهم ومنادمهم ،
وسيد القوم خادمهم ، اعلم من له هه ، كيف تكون
شروط لخدمه ، اشد لخدمة وسطى ، واوثق بالعزيمة
شرطى ، ولا ازال واقفا على قدم ، وكذلك وظيفة من
خدم ، لا اجلس بين جلاسى ، ولا ارفع الى النديم
راسى ، ولا امنع الطالب طيب انفاسى ، ولست لعهد
من وصلنى ناسى ، ولا على من قطعنى قاسى ، ثم
لا يفارق فى شربى كاسى ، وكاسى بصفوه لى كاسى ، بنى
على قضب الزمرد اساسى ، وجعل من اللجين والعجب
لباسى ، اتلمح تقصيرى فاطرق اطراق الخجل ، وافكر
فى مصيرى فاحدق لهجوم الاجل ، ومن العجب انى
واقف على التفرقة فى مقام الجمع ، يدرك معنا شذاى
حاسة الشم لا حاسة السمع ، وهذا معنى لم يخطر بقلب
ولا يمر بسمع، فاطراقى اعتراف بتقصيرى، واطلاقى نظر
الى ما فيه مصيرى ،

شعر

ان يكن منى دنى اجلى

آه يا ذلى ويا خجلى

قمت من ذل على قدمى

مطرقا بالراس من زللى

لو بذلت الروح مجتهـدا

ونفيت النوم عن مقلى

كنت بالتقصير معترفا

خائفا من خيبة الامـلى

ان يكن للعبد سابقة

سبقت فى الاعصر الاولى

لم يكن فى النادمين غـدا

نافعى علمى ولا عمـلى

مقلى انسانـها ابـدا

قط لا يرتـد فى اجلى

عجلا فى خيفة وكـذا

خلـق الانسان من عجـلى

ⵎⵎⵎⵎ

اشارة اللينوفر

فنادى اللينوفر، وحظه من السقم اوفى واوفر، اما
تعتبر ايها الحزين باصفرارى، واين من القدر فرارى،
انا الذى قد رضيت بعارى، ولست من العشق بعارى،
الرياض دارى، والغياض قرارى، فان كنت عاشقـا
فدارىٌّ، ها انا اعشق صفا الماء الجارى، فلا افارقه
صباحا ولا مساء، ولا صيفا ولا شتا، ومن العجب اني به
ولهان، وعليه لهفان، واليه ظمان وانا معه حيث كان،
فهل سمعتم بمثل هذا الشان، واقف فى الما عطشان، افتح
عينى بالنهار، فيغار علىّ من الاغيار، فاذا جن ليلى،
انزلنى عن رتبتى وحطّنى، واخذنى اليه وغطّنى،
فاغوص الى وكرى، واعود الى خلوة فكرى، وتستغرق
عينى، فى مشاهدة قرة عينى، فلا يعرف للجهول اينى،
ولا يفرق العذول بين من احبه وبينى، فحيث مال بى
هواى، لا انظره الا احداى، ان ظمئت ارواى، وان

اوبت اليه اوانى، فحياة وجودى بحيانه، وبقا شهودى
بثبانه، وتمام ذاق بذاته، وصفا صفاتى بصفاته، فا
بيننا بين، ولولاه ما كنت لا اثر ولا عين،

شعر

كسى لحب جسمَ ثوب الفنا
فروحِ من شوقـها فى عـنا
كانّ الهــوى اذ رمى سهــه
لقلبىَ دون الورى قـد عـنا
تـدانى فادنى الى اضلـعى
هوى كلما قـد دنا قَـدَّنَا
بـقيت لـه فى فـنـاى بـه
وابقى لىَ الوجد ذاك الـفـنا
يقول لىَ لحـب لا تـالـفَـنْ
سوانا اذا رمـت منى الغـنا
حمينا الوصال بحـد النـصال
فان تلـق سمر القنا تلـقنا
فلا تجـزعنّ لحر النـبـال
ومر النكال ففيه الـهـنا

ومت مثل ما مات اهل الهوى

وذابوا اشتياقا فنالوا المنــا

وما ضرّهم حيـــن نــاداهُم

عـلى طـور سـيـنـاء انى انـا

〰〰〰〰

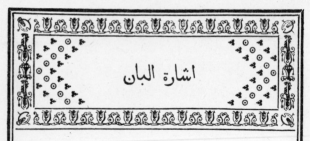

اشارة البان

فلما نظر الاشجار الى طرب البان ببينهم ، وتمايله
دونهم ، لاموه على كثرة تمايله ، وعنّفوه على اعجابه
بتمائله ، فتمايل هنالك البان ، وقال قد ظهر عذرى
وبان ، فمَنْ ذا يلومنى على تمايل اغصانى ، واهتزاز
اركانى ، وانا الذى بسطت لى الارض مطارفها ، واظهرت
لى الرياض زخارفها ، واهدت لى نسمات الاسحار لطائفها
وظرائفها ، فاذا رايت ساعة نشور اموات النبات قد
اقتربت ، ورايت الارض قد اهتزت وربت ، ونفخ فى
صور وعدى ، ونسخ حكم وعيدى باتجاز وعدى ، وحان
ورود وردى ، فانظر الى المورد وقد ورد ، والى البرد
وقد شرد ، والى الزهر وقد انـقـد ، والى الحب وقد
انعقد ، والى الغصن اليابس وقد كسى بعد ما انجرد ،
والى اختلاف المطاعم والمشارب وقد اتحد ، فاعلم ان
صانعها واحد احد ، وصاحبها صمد ، وموجدها بالقدرة

قد انفرد ، فلا يفتقر الى احد ، ولا يستغنى عنه احد ، ولا يشاركه فى ملكه احد ، الذى لم يلد ولم يولد ، ولم يكن له كفوا احد ، فهنالك تمايلت قدودى ، طربا بطيب شهودى ، وتبلبلت بلابل سعودى ، على تحريك عودى ، ثم تداركنى عناية معبودى ، فافكر فى عدم وجودى ، وفوات مقصودى ، فانعطف على الورد فاخبره بورودى ، واخلع عليه من برودى ، واستخبره اين مقصدى وورودى ، فقال لى وجودك كوجودى ، وركوعك كسجودى ، انت بخضرة قدودك ، وانا بحمزة خدودى ، فهلم نجعل فى النار وقودك ووقودى ، قبل نار خلودك وخلودى ، فقلت له. اذا صح الائتلاف ، ورضيت لنفسك بالتلاف ، فليس للخلاف خلاف ، فنقتطف على حكم الوفاق ، ونختطف من بين الرفاق ، فتصعد انفاسنا بالاحتراق ، وتقطر دموعنا بلا اشفاق ، فاذا فنينا على صور اشباحنا بقينا بمعانى ارواحنا ، فشتّان بين غدونا ورواحنا ،

شعر

ورد الورد بشيــرا بـالـذى
فيه من لطف المعانى قد حــوى

فانثنى البان له منعطـفـا

لائم النشر الذى فيه انطـوى

مال يشكو اهيفُ القـد لـه

فرط ما يلقاه من جور الهـوى

فرثاه الـورد اذ قــال لــه

نحن خلّان تقاسمنــا لجــوى

فانا انت كــمـا انـت انــا

نحن فى المعنا جميعا بالسـوى

كم رمينا فى لظـى نـار ولا

صاحبى ضلّ ولا قلـبى غــوى

ولكم قد فرقت ايدى النـوى

بيننا والغصن منـا مـا ذوى

لو ترى احشاءنا قد حشيـت

بلهيب النار والقلب انـكـوى

وبها انفسنا قــد صعـدت

مثل ما قد قطرت منا القـوى

كلنا نشكو بـنجـو واحــد

ولكـل فى هــواه مـانــوى

قسما حقا بميـنـا صادقـا

بالذى قَدْمَا فِىَ العرش استــوى

ان فى شــرح غـرامى عـــبـــرة

لذوى القلب اذا القلب ارعوى

كنت بالامس كبـدر طـالــع

وانا اليوم كنجم قــــد هـــوى

اشارة البنفسج

فتنفس البنفسج تنفس الصعدا، وتاوّه تاوّه البعدا،
وقال طوبى لمن عاش عيش السعدا، ومـــات مـوت
الشهدا، الى كم اذوب بالـذبول كمدا، واكتسى
بالنحول اثوابا جددا، افنتنى الايام فما اطالت لى
امدا، وغيرتنى الاحكام فما ابقت لى جلدا ولا جَلَدا،
فما اقصر ما قضيت عيشا رغدا، وما اطول ما بقيت
يابسا مجردا، وجملـة خصولى، انــى اوخـذ ايام
حصولى، فاقطع من اصولى، وامنع من وصولى، وكم
ممـن يتقوى على ضعـفى، ويعسف بى مع ترفى
ولطفى وظرفى ، فينتـنعم بى من حضرنى ، ويجتلبينى
من نظرنى ، ثم لا البث الا يوما او بعض يوم ، حتى
اسام بانجس سوم ، ويعاد علىّ بعد الثنا باللوم ، فامسى
مما لقيت ممعوكا ، وبايدى لحوادث معروكا ، فاذا اصبحت
يابسا، ومن النضارة ايسا، اخذنى اهل المعانى ، ومن
هو لحكم يعانى، فتفشش بى الاورام الفاشية، وتلين

بى الآلام القاسية، وتلطف بى الطبائع العاتية، وتدفع
بدوائ الادواء العادية، فالناس ممتعون بيابسى ورطبى،
جاهلون بعظم خطبى، غافلون عما اودع بى من حكم
ربى، وانى لمن يتدبرنى عبرة لمن اعتبر، وتذكرة لمن
اذكر، وفى مزدجر لمن ازدجر، حكمة بالغة فما تغنى
النذر،

شعر

ولقد عجبت من البنفسج اذ غدا
يحكى باوراق على اغـــصـانـــه
جيشا طوارقه الزبرجد رصعت
احجار ياقوت على خـــرصانـه
فكـــانـما اعـــداوه بجـــلادة
شيلت رُؤسهم على عـــيـــدانه

اشارة المنثور

فناداه منظوم المنثور، بنقشه المغرور، ونفسه المصدور، ورقشه المبثور، وقال ما هذا الغرور، بالعمر المبتور، وما هذا السرور، بالعيش المكدور، اما تعتبر بغصنى المائل، ولونى لحائل، وعمرى الزائل، وايامى القلائل غيرتنى حوادث الايام، وقسمت لونى على ثلاثة اقسام، فنى الاصفر كسى من السقم ثوبا معصفرا، فكان كالعشاق منظرا ومخبرا، ومنى الابيض اليقق، كسى ثوب القلق، من الفرق، ومنى الازرق، الذى كاد بكمه يحترق، فاما الابيض فلا يفوح عطره، ولا يلوح بشره، ولا ينشق نشره، ولا يكشف ستره، لانه كتم سره فما باح، واخفى عطره فما فاح، وملك امره فلا تلعب به الاهواء والرياح، واما الاصفر فخلع العذار واستراح، وتوشح من السقم بوشاح، وفاح عطره فى الغدو والرواح، وصعد انفاس نشره فى المسا والصباح،

شعر

ما نفحت من ارضكم نسمة
الا وسح الدمع شجوا وساح
لولاكمُ يا اهل ذاك الحمى
ما راح قلبى موثقا بالجراح
اسرتم القلب ويكـفيكمُ
لا تقتلونى قد رميت السلاح

ان غلب علىّ وجدى ، وبحت بما عندى ، فليس على
العاشق جناح

شعر

لا تلحنى ان بدا منى افتضاح
ما على العاشق ان باح جناح

واما الازرق فانطوى على جواه ، وصبر على اذاه ،
وكم بالنهار شذاه ، وقال انا لا ابوح بسرى لعاشق ، ولا
افوح بالنهار لناشق ، فاذا جنّ ليلى ابديت ما بى
لاحبابى ، وشكوت مصابى ، لاهل اوصابى ، فاذا دارت
الكووس شربت كاسى ، واذا طابت النفوس صعدت

انفاسى ، فانا لجلاسى ، كالخليل المواسى ، ومتى دعيت
لإيناس ، جيت اسعى على راسى ، والى الله اشكوا ما
اقاسى ، من القلب القاسى ، وماكتمت بالنهار عطرى ،
واخترت فى الليل هتك سترى ، الا لان الليل خلوة
العشاق ، وجلوة كل مشتاق ، وغيبة الرقيب ، وحضرة
الحبيب ، فاذا قال هل من سائل ، جعلت اليه انفاسى
رسائل ، وذلى لعزه وسائل ،

شعر

أصعّد انفاس شوق اليـــه
واوقــف طيب ثنـاى عليه
ومالى الى وصلـه شـافـع
سوى حسن ظنى وذلى لديه
وقلبى فى تخطـه والـــرضى
سواء فما حال عن حالتيه

أشارة الياسمين

فصاح بفصاحته الياسمين ، وقال ان الياس مين ،
ويحك انا أَفُوحُ بوقاحة روحى من الرياحين ، واتردد
الى الاحباب حينا بعد حين ، اجلب مـن خـزايـن
الغيوب ، فلا اسكن الا فى كمايـن لجيوب ، ابوح بسرى
ايما حضرت ، وافوح بعطرى ايما خطرت ، لا اخفى
على ذى ذوق ، ولا يتكرنى من له شوق ، فريحى على
الرياحين يعلوا ، ونـشرى على الازاهير يسمـوا ، لانّ
من طاب معناه كان اطيب وازكى ، ومن بـه دعواه كان
اظهر واذكى ، فمن اراد مراتب العلا فليـعـالِ
بلطافة معاليه ، وليبرق فى درج معانيه ، ومـن قصر
فى تدانبه ، لم يفز بامانيه ، وقّ اشاره ، وحقيقتها
للطالبين بشاره ، فـاول اسمى يـاس واخره مين ،
فالياس مين ، والمين شين ، فلما اجتمع ياس ومين ،
دلا على ببينونة البين ، وبشر بقرة العين ،

شعر

رايت الفال بشرنى بخير
وقد اهدى الىّ الياسـمـين
فلا تحزن فان الحزن شين
ولا تيأس فان الياس مين

~~~~~~~~

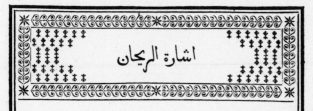

اشارة الريحان

فقال الريحان ، قد آن حضورى وحان ، نحـذنى خذبها، واتخذنى نديها، فرطيب خـضرتى ، تخبر عن طيب حضرتى ، فكيف تسترح روح بغير ريحان ، ام كيف يلذ سماع بغير لحان ، انا الموعود فى الجنان ، السارى بانفاس الى صيم الجـنـان ، فـلـونى اعدل الالوان، وكونى الطف الاكوان،مَنْ جَنَانى مِنْ جِنانى، استنشق نشرى المطوى فى جَنانى ، فانا اليف الانهار، وحليف الازهار، وجليس السمار، وكاتم الاسرار، فان سمعت فى جنسى بالمام ، فلا تكن له لوام ، فانه ما نم الا على عطره ، وما باح الا بسره ، وما فـاح الا بنشره، وباح بسره أُعلاما، ونشر مِنْ نشره إِعلاما، فلذلك سمى نماما ، وليس من نم على نفسه ،كمن نم على غيره، ولا من جاد بخبره،كمن جاد بضبره ، ولكن جفت الاقلام ، وجرت الاحكام ، بان النمام ، مذموم بين الانام ، والسلام ،

شعر

سايلى عن خفى سر غرامى
وَيْك اقصر و خلنى وهيـامى
انا مستودع لسر حـبـيـبى
كيف ابدى ولست بالنمامى

~~~~~~

اشارة الاخوان

فنادى على نفسه الاخوان ، وهو بما كسى من النضارة فرحان ، وقال قد آن ظهورى ، وحان حضورى ، واعتدل فصل وجودى ، وطاب فى الحضرة شهودى ، وكيف لا يطيب وقتى ، وهذه الانهار تجرى من تحتى ، وكيف لا اودّى بالشكر زكاة حولى، وقد تم نصاب حولى ، و ما ذاك من قوتى ولا حولى ، فبياضى هو العلم المعلم ، واصفرارى هو السقم المبرم ، واختلاف الوانى هو المتشابه المحكم ، فان كنت للرموز تفهم ، فقم الى تنعم ، والّا نم ، وان كنت لا تدرى ما ثم ، فحقيق ان يقام عليك مأتم ،

شعر

اذا لم تدرك المعنى وتدرى
خفايا ما اقول فلا تلمنى
نعتنك مشفقا بلسان حالى

وما يغنيك شرح الحال عنى
اما يكفيك حولى كل حول
وما نالته ايدى الدهر منى
فكم وافيتنى فى جمع شمل
زمانا ثم جمَّت فلم تجدنى
حمام الايك يسعفنى اذاما
شكوت اليه انجانى يجبنى
ينوح علىَّ عن علم بشانى
ملقَّا للفناء بكل فتَّى
وانت تظنه طربا ولهوا
فتمرح بين عيدانى وغصنى
حقيق ان يناح عليك اذ لم
تفرَّق بين افراحى وحزنى

~~~~~~

فلما رأى الخزام، ما يكابده الزهر من القيد والالتزام،
فمنها ما يضام، وينشر بعد النظام، وبالثمن البخس
يسام، قال انا ما لى والزحام، لا اعاشر اللئام، ولا
اسمع قول اللوام، والزمت من بين الازهار، ان لا
اجاور الانهار، ولا اقف على شفا جرف هار، ارافق
الوحش فى النفار، واسكن البرارى والقفار، احب
الخلوات، واستوطن الفلوات، فلا ازاحم فى المحافل،
ولا اتحمل منّة الزارع والكافل، ولا تقطفنى ايدى
الاسافل، ولا احمل الى اللاعب والهازل، لكنّنى
بعيد عن المنازل، تجدنى فى ارض نجد نازل، رضيت
بالبر الفسيح، وقنعت بمجاوزة الغزال والشيح، تعبق
بنشرى الريح، فتحملنى الى ذوى التقديس والتسبيح،
لا ينشقنى الا من له ذوق صحيح، وشوق صريح، وهو
على زهد المسيح، وصبر الذبيح، فانا رفيق السواح،

فى الغدوّ والرواح ، فافوز بالاجور ، واسلم من حضور
اهل الفجور، فلا احضر على منكر، ولا اجلس عند
من يشرب ويسكر، فانا للحرّ الذى لا يـبــاع فى
الاسواق ، ولا ينادى على بالنفّاق ، فى سوق النفاق ،
ولا تحضرنى الفُسّاق ، ولا ينظرنى الا من شمر عن ساق ،
وركب جواد العزيمة وساق ، فلو رايتنى فى البوادى ،
والنسيم يهيم بى فى كل وادى ، اعطر البادى ، بعطر
البادى ، واروح الــنــادى ، بنشرى النادى ،
ان عرض بذكرى للحادى ، حن اليه كل رايح وغادى ،

شعر

يحدّثـنـى النـسيم عن الخزامـا

ويقرينى عن الشيخ الـسـلامـا

فهمت بما فهمت وطـبـت وجـدا

فما احـلاه لى لو كان دامـا

ويسرى تحت جنح الليـل سـرّا

فيوقظنى وقـد جمع النـدامـا

واسكرنى شذاها حين هبـت

كانى قد ترشفت المـدامـا

يعــارضــنى بانــفــاس مــراض

كــانــفــاسى وقد ملبت غــرامـــا

وقد عُرفَت بطيب العـرف لمـا

كساها اللطفى اخلاقا كرامـــا

اهيم بنــشــرها طــربــا ووجــدا

فيبدى البرق عن طربى ابتساما

تمر على الريــاض بــارض نجــد

فتنعطف الغصون لها احتشاما

يقلّقنى حمــام الايــك نــوحــا

وبذكـرى المنازل والخيــامـــا

خيام تجــمــع الاحــبــاب فيها

وفيها يبلــغ القلب المــرامـــا

تجلّى وجه مــن اهــواه فــيــها

بحسن نورُه يجــلــو الــظــلامــا

〜〜〜〜〜〜

اشارة الشقيق

فتنفس الشقيق بين ندمائه، وهو مصرح بدمائه،
واستوى على ساقه ووثب، وقال يا لله العجب، ما بال
لونى باهى، وحسنى زاهى، وقدرى بين الرياحين
واهى، فلا احد بى يباهى، ولا ناظر الىّ ساهى، فليت
شعرى ما الذى اسقط جاهى، ارفل فى ثوبى القاذى،
وانا مدحوض عند من يلقانى؛ فلا انا فى الحضرة حاضر،
ولا يشار الىّ بالنواظر، ولا اصافح بالمناخر، وما برحت
فى عدد الرياحين اخر، فانا طريد عن حمى، بعيد
عن قربى، وما اظن ذلك الا من سواد قلبى، فلا حول
لى فى قضا ربى، فلما رايت باطنى محشوا بالذنوب،
وقلبى مسودا بالعيوب، علمت ان الله تعالى لا ينظر الى
الصور ولكن ينظر الى القلوب، فكان اعجابى باثوابى،
سببا لحجابى عن ثوابى، فكنت كالرجل المنافق الذى
حسنت سيرته، وقبحت سريرته، وراق فى المنظر
سمته، وقل فى الخبر قيمته، ولو صلح قلبى لصلح

امرئ ، ولو شاء ربى لطاب بين الخلائق ذكرى ، وفاح بين الازاهير نشرى ، لكن الطيب لا يفوح الا ممن يطيب ، وعلامات القبول لا تلوح الا على من رضى عنه الحبيب، ويحقّ لمن اصبح فى هواه كئيب ، وفى معناه سليب، ان يندب عليه بالنحيب، ويبكى عليه بالدمع الصبيب ،

شعر

لا تلحنى اذا شققت ردائئُ

فلامى يزيد فى الحب دائئُ

انا قلبى قد سودته ذنوبى

وقفا لى معذبى بشقائئُ

من رآنى يظن خيرا ولكنى

خالقى عالم بأنى مرائئُ

قد تحسنت منظرا ولباسا

ورزايا محشوة بحشاى

واحيانئُ اذا سُئلت وما لى

من جواب وانجلتى واحيانئُ

لوكشفت الستور عن سوء حالى

لرايت السرور للاعدائئُ

اشارة السحاب

فلما حسن العتاب ، وطاب فصل الخطاب ، دمع
السحاب ، فانبسط وساح فى فسيح الرحاب ، وقال
سبحان الله اينكر فضلى عليكم ، وانا الباعث
ظلى وويلى البكم ، وهل انتم الا الاطفال جودى ،
ونسل وجودى ، كم ملأت البر برًّا بيرى ، والبحر
ذُرا بدَرى ، انا مغذى نطف البذر فى بطن امه ،
ومستخرجه بالقوة من غمه ، فاذا تخضت الحوامل بحملها،
واستخرجت بنات النبات من حفرة رملها ، جعلت
حوالته الى ، وحضانته على ، فلم يزل ثدى درى عليه
درارا ، ومزيد برى اليه مدرارا ، فاذا انقضت ايام
الرضاع و لم يبقَ الا الفطام ، فاقطع ثديى عنه فيصبح
لاهل الدنيا حطام ، فكان بعثه فى انسكاب عبراتى ،
ونشوره فى بعث قطراتى ، فالكل فى الحقيقة اطفالى ، ولو
اعترفوا بحقى لكانوا من الجو اطفالى ، وقد سمع كل
حىّ فى حىّ ، وجعلنا من الماء كل شىء حىّ ،

شعر

واذا نظرت لربعها العطالى

فابكى عليه بدمعك الهطّالى

يبكى المشوق اذا البروق تبسمت

ووشت اليه نسائمُ الامـالى

فتنفس الصعدا من وجد له

متلفتا لدوارس الاطـلالى

لا تعذلنه على جواه ولا تلـ

ـه على هواه فليس عنه بسالى

واترك مقاومة الغرام فانـه

فيه اللهيب وما به بلـبالى

‌ش‌ش‌ش‌ش‌ش‌ش

اشارة الهزار

قال فبينما انا مصغٍ لمنادمة ازهارها، على حافات
انهارها، اذ صاحت فصاحة اطيارها من اوكارها،
فاول ما صوّت الهزار، ونادى على نفسه بخلع العذار،
وباح بما يكاتمه من الاسرار، وقال بلسان حاله انا
العاشق الولهان، الهائم اللهفان، الصادى الظمان،
اذا رايت فصل الربيع قد حان، ومنظره البديع قد
آن، تجدّني فى الرياض فرحان، وفى الغياض اردد
الالحان، اغنى واطرب، وادير الكاس علىّ فاشرب، فانا
بنغمتى طربان، ومن نشوتى سكران، فاذا زمزم النسيم
وصفقت اوراق الاغصان، ارقص على العيدان، فكانما
الزهر والنهر لى عيدان، وانت تحسبنى فى ذلك عاشقا
عابثا، لا والله ولست فى اليمين حانثا، وانما انوح حزنا
لا طربا، وابوح ترحا لا فرحا، لانى ما وجدت روضة
الا تبلبلت على بلابلها، ولا نزهة الانحت على اضمحلالها،
ولا حضرة الا بكيت على زوالها، فانى ما رايت صفوة

الاّ تكدرت ، ولا عيشة حلوة الا تمررت ، فقرات فى
مثال العرفان ، كل من عليها فان ، فكيف لا انوح
على حال يحول ، ووقت يدول ، وعيش يزول ، ووصل
عن قريب مفصول ، وهذه الجملة من شرح حالى تغنى
من الفصول ،

شعر

حديث ذاك الحمى روحى وريحانى

فلا تلمنى اذا كـــررت الحـــانى

روض به الراح والريحان قد جمعا

وحضرة ما لها فى حسنها اثانى

من ابيض يقق او اصفر فـقـع

او اخضر رقـق او احمـر قـانى

والنهر والزهر والاغصان ترقص فى

ميدان عشقى على اوتار عيدانى

والوصل دان وشمل الوصل مجتمـع

هذا هو العيش الا انـه فـانى

اشارة الباز

فنادى الباز، وهو فى ميدان البراز، ويحك لقد صغر
جِرْمك، وكبر جَرْمك، ولقد اقلقت بتغريدك الطير،
واطلاق لسانك يجلب اليك الضير، وما يفضى بـك
الى خير، اوما علمت ان ما يهلك الانسان، الا عثرات
اللسان، فلولا لقلقة لسانك، ما اخذت من بين
اقرانك، وحبست فى ضيق الاقفاص، وسد عليك
باب الخلاص، وهل ذلك الا بما جناه عليك لسانك،
فافتتح به بيانك، فلو اهتديت بصمتى، واقتديت
بصمتى، لبرئت من الملامه، وعلمت ان الصمت رفيق
السلامه، الم ترَ بى لزمت الصموت، والفت السكوت،
فكان الصمت جمالى، ولزوم الادب كمالى، اقتنصت
من البرّية جبرا، وجلبت الى بلاد الغربة قهرًا، فلا
بالسريرة بحت، ولا على الاطلال نحت، بل اذّبت
حين غرّبت، وقرّبت حين جرّبت، وامتنحت حين

امتحنت، وعند الامتحان، يُكرم المرء او يُهان، فلما رای مودبی تخليط الوقت، خاف علىّ من المقت، فكمّ بصری بكُمّةٍ لا تهدّنّ عينيك، وعقد لسانی بعقدةٍ لا تحرّك به لسانك، وقيدنی بقيدٍ ولا تمشِ فی الارض مرحا، فانا من وثاقٍ متالم، ومِا الاقی لا اتكلم، فلما كممت وادبت، وجربت وهذبت، استصلحنی مودبی لارسالی الی الصيد، وزال عنی ذلك القيد، فاطلقت وارسلت، باشارةٍ انّا ارسلناك، فما رفعت الكمة عن عينی، حتی اصلحت ما بينه وبينی، فوجدتُ الملوك خدّامی، واكفهم تحت اقدامی،

شعر

امسكت عن فضل الكلام لسانی
وكففت عن نظر الدُنا انـــــــــــسانی
ما ذاك الا ان قرب مـنـيّـــتی
لزخارف اللـــذات قد انـسانی
أدّبتُ آداب الملوك وعــلّـــمـــت
روحی هناك صنائعَ الاحـــسانی
ارسلت مـن كف الملوك مجردا

وجعلت ما ابغيه نصب عيــانى

حتى ظفرت ونلت ما املــتــه

ثم استجبت اليه حــين دعــانى

هذا لعرى رسم كل مكلــف

بوظايف التسـلـيم لــلايمانى

〜〜〜〜

اشارة الحمام

قال فبينما انا مستغرق فى لذة كلامه، معتبر بحكمه
واحكامه، اذ رايت امامه حمامه، قد جعل طوق
العبودية فى عنقها علامه، فقلت لها حدثينى عن
ذوقك وشوقك، واوصى لى ما للحكمة فى تطويق
طوقك، فقالت انا المطوقة بطوق الامانه، المقلدة
بتقليد الصيانه، نُدبت لحمل الرسايل، وتبليغ
الوسايل للسايل، ولكنى اخبرك عن القصة العجيبه،
فان الدين النصيحه، ماكل طاير امين، ولا كل حالى
يصدق فى اليمين، ولا كل سالك من اصحاب اليمين،
انما المخصوص بحمل الامانة جنسى، وما ابرى نفسى،
يحمل الامانة من الطير ماكان ابلق واخضر، لانه
احسن فى المنظر، واعدل فى المخبر، فاذا كان الطاير
اسود دل على تجاوز الطبيعه حد النصيحه، وان كان
ابيض دل على قصور الطبيعة عن حد النصيحه،

فيدل على انحراف المزاج عن الاعتدال ، وقصر الهمة
عن بلوغ الامال ، ولا تكون الهمة العليه ، الا فى الروح
الزكيه ، ولا شرف العزيمه ، الا فى النفس النفيسة
المستقيمه ، واذا اعتدل لون الطائر دل على اعتدال
تركيبه ، ويصلح حينئذ لتقريبه وتاديبه ، فيشترى
بالتقريب ، ويعرف الطريق بالتدريج ، فاقول حملونى
فاحمل كتب الاسرار ، ولطائف الرسائل والاخبار ،
فاطير ، وعقلى مستطير ، خايفا من جارح جارح ،
حاذرا من سابح سابح ، جازعا من صايد ذابح ، فاهاجر ،
واكابد الظما فى الهواجر ، واطوى على الطوى فى
الهاجر ، فلو رايت حبة قمح مع شدة جوعى رجعت
عنها ، وذكرت ما جرى على ادم منها فارتفع خشيةً
من كمين فى مدفون ، او شرك يعيقنى عن تبليغ
الرسالة فانقلب بصفقة المغبون ، فاذا وصلت ، وفى
مامنى حصلت ، اديت ما حُملت ، واخبرت ما عُلمت ،
فهنالك طوقت ، وبالبشارة خلقت ، وانقلب الى شكر
الله على ما وفقت ،

شعر

احبابى وصلــتم او هجــرتم

فعبدكم على حفظ الامانه

مقيم لا يزحزحــه عــنـول

ولا يثنى معنفه عــنــانــه

حملت لاجلكم ما ليس تقوى

جبال الشم تحملــه رزانــه

وحفظ العهد ما وافاه حر

وطـوّقــه فــتى الّا وزانــه

فدعه وحب من بهـوى والا

فشانك يا معنفه وشــانــه

<hr />

اشارة لخطاف

قال فبينما نحن نتذاكر اوصاف الاشراف ،
واشراف الاوصاف ، اذ نظرت الى خطاف ، وهو
بالبيت قد طاف ، فقلت ما لى اراك للبيوت لازما ،
وعلى موانسة الانس عازما ، فلو كنت فى امرك حازما
لما فارقت ابناء جنسك ، ورضيت فى البيوت بحبسك ،
ثم انك لا تنزل الا فى المنازل العامره ، والمساكـن
التى هى باهلها عامره ، فـقال يا كثـيف الطبع ،
يا ثقيل السمع ، اسمع ترجمة حالى ، وكيف عن الطير
ارتحالى ، انا فارقت امثالى ، وعاشرت غير اشكالى ،
واستوطنت السقوف ، دون الشعاب والكهوف ، الا
لفضيلة الغربه ، ولزوما لاداب العبه ، حببت من
ليس منى لاكون غريبا ، وجاورت خيرا منى ليصير
لى بينهم نصيبا ، فاعيش عيش الغربا ، وافوز بعبة
الادبا ، والغريب مرحوم فى غربته، ملطوف به فى

هبته، فقصدت المنازل ، غير مضرّ بالنازل ، ابتنى
بيتى من حافات الانهار، واكتسب قوتى من ساحات
القفار، فلست للجار كمن جار، ولا لاهل الدار كالغدار،
بل احسن جوارى مع جارى، وليس منهم رسم جارى ،
اكثر سوادهم ، ولا استطعم زادهم ، فزهدى فيما فى
ايديهم ، هو الذى حببنى اليهم ، فلو شاركتهم فى قوتهم،
لما بقيت معهم فى بيوتهم ، فانا شربكهم فى انديـتهم ،
لا فى اغديتهم ، مزاحم فى اوقاتهم ، لا فى اقواتهم ،
مكتسب من اخلاقهم ، لا من ارزاقهم ، منتهب من
حالهم ، لا من مالهم ، مقتبس من برهم، لا من بُرهم ،
راغب فى حبهم ، لا فى حَبهم ، مقتديا فى ذلك باشارة
صاحب الاشارة صلى الله عليه وسلم ازهد فى الدنيا
يحبك الله وازهد فيما فى ايدى الناس يحبك الناس ،

شعر

كن زاهدا فيها حوته يد الورى
تعفى الى كل الانام حبيــبــا
اوما ترى للخطــاف حرم زادهم
فغدا ربيبا فى الجور قـريبا

قال فقلت لله درك لقد عشت سعيداً، وسرت سيراً
حميداً، ووفقت امراً رشيداً، وقلت قولاً سديداً،
فلا اطلب على موعظتك مزيداً .

اشارة البوم

قال فنادانى البوم، وهو منفرد فى الخراب مهموم،
ايها الصديق الصادق، والخـل المـرافـق، لا تكن
بمقالة للخطاف واثقا، ولا لفعله موافـقـا، فانـه ان
سلم من شبه زادهم، فما سلم من نزه فرحهم واعيادهم،
وتكثير سوادهم، وقد علمت ان من كثر سواد قوم فهو
منهم، ولو جمعهم ساعة كان مسئولا عنهم، وقد فهمت
ان مبتدا التفريط، من افات التخليط، والخلطة غلطه،
واول السيل نقطه، واعلم ان السلامة فى العزله،
فمن وليها فلا يخاف عزله، فهلا استنسّ بسنتى، وتاسّى
بوحدتى، واعتزل المنازل والنازل، وازهد فى الماكل
والآكل، الا ترانى لا اشاركهم فى منازلهم، ولا اجالسهم
فى مجالسهم، ولا اساكنهم فى مساكنهم، ولا ازاحمهم
فى اماكنهم، بل اخترت الداثر من الجدران، ورضيت
بالخراب عن العمران، فسلمت من الانكاد، وامنت
من الحساد، ولم ازل عن الاحباب وحيدا، ومن القرنا

فريدا، وعن الاتراب بعيدا غريبا، فمن كان مسكنه
التراب، كيف يساكن الاتراب، من كان الليل
والنهار يخربان عمره كيف لا يقنع بالخراب، من علم
ان العمر وان طال قصير، وان كلا الى الفنا يصير،
بات على خشن لحصير، وافطر على قرص الشعير،
ورضى من الدنيا باليسير، وعلم ان فريقا فى الجنة
وفريقا فى السعير، انا نظرت الى الدنيا وخرابها،
والى الاخرة واقترابها، والى القيامة وحسابها، والى
النفس واكتسابها، فشغلنى التفكر فى حالى، عن
منزلى لحالى، واذهلنى ما علي وما لى، واذهبنى عن
اهلى ومالى، واهمنى همتى واعتلالى، عن القصور العوالى،
لجلا اليقين عن نظر بصرى كل شبهه، فعلمت ان لا
فرحة تدوم ولا نزهه، وانه كل شى هالك الا وجهه،
فعرفت من هو، وما عرفت ما هو، وحيث كنت فلا
ارى الا هو، فاذا نطقت فلا اقول الا هو،

شعر

افردنى عنـــم هـــواه
وليس لى مقصد ســواه

اهيم وحدى بصدق وجدى

وحسن قصدى عمى اراه

انكر حبى غرام قلبى

وما دروا بالـــذى دهاه

احببت مـولى اذا تجــلّى

اقتبس البدر من ســناه

تميـز الناس فـيـه طرّا

وجملة لخلق فــيــه تاهوا

ولا اسمـيـه غـــيـــر انى

ان غلب الوجد قلت يا هو

قال فاخذت موعظته بجامع قلبى، وخلعت عنى ملابس
عجـــبى، الا ان الـهوى يقول بُحْ بى،

———

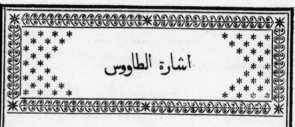

اشارة الطاووس

قال ثم التفت فرايت طاووسا ، وقد شرب من خمرة
العجب كووسا ، وقد لبس من ملابس التلبيس ، وهو
الذى عاد عليه شوم ابليس ، قد زين ريشه الوان ،
وفنن عيشه افنان ، لا ياوى الى الجنان ، واسه اعلم ما
فى الجنان ، فقلت له ويحك كم بينك وبين البوم ،
فى الحظ المقسوم ، انت ايها العانى ، نظرت فى الصور
وهو نظر فى المعانى ، واغتررت بالامانى وفرحت
بالفانى ، فقال لى يا عانى ، يا من هو بالشماتة نعانى ،
لاتظهرلى الشماته ، ولا تذكر للحزين ما فاته ، فقد
قيل فى الخبر ، ارحموا عزيز قوم ذل وغنى قوم افتقر ،
اين كنت وانا فى الجنان اطوف ، بين الجداول والقطوف ،
وادور دورها ، وادخل قصورها ، وازور ولدانها ،
وحورها ، شرابى التسبيح وطعامى التقديس ، حتى ساق
القدر المقدور الى ابليس ، فالبسنى ملابس التلبيس ،
وعوضنى بالخسيس عن النفيس ، هذا وانا لمراده كاره ،

ولكن القدر يوقع فى المكاره ، وينفر الطير عن
أوكاره ، ولقد كانت ابليس يرفل فى حلل قربه ، فما
تركه هوم رايه حتى تاه على ادم بعجبه، وكانت لى معه فى
تلك القضيه ، قصة غير مرضيه ، فاوقعنى فى الخطيه ،
وما اطلعنى على ما له من خبث الطويه ، غير انى كنت
له دلاله ، وكانت الحية فى دخوله للجنة محتاله ، فاخرجت
معهم من ديار العز الى ديار الأذلال ، وقيل هذه اجرة
الدلال ، وجزاء من عاشر الانذال ، ثم ابقيت علىّ زينة
ربى ، أتذكر بها ما كان من صفو عيشى ، فيزيدنى
ذلك تحرقا وتشوقا ، والى الجنة تلهفا وتتوقا ، ثم جعلت
علامة الخط فى ساقى ، لانظرها كل حين باعماقى ،
وينادى علىّ بنقض ميثاقى ، ثم الفت من البقاع
بقعة تشاكل ما اخرجت منه ، وطردت بشقاوتى عنه ،
فاتذكر بالبساتين مرابع ربوعى ، واجرى عليها
سواكب دموعى ، والوم نفسى التى كانت سبب وقوعى ،
واقول كلما تذكرت تفريق جموعى ،

شعر

يا دار هل يقضى لنا برجوعى

ويعود لى يا عين طيب هجوعى

يا سادة كاد المشوق لبينهم

يبقى اسا فى ساعة التوديعى

قلبى ليوم فراقكم متوجع

وارحمتاه لقلبى الموجوعى

فرقتموا ما بين جفنى والكرى

ووصلتموا بين الاسا وضلوعى

جسمى معى والقلب بين خيامكم

ما ضركم لو كان ثم جميعى

واذا ذكرت ليالىا سلفت لنا

فى وصل احبابى وظل ربوعى

فاكاد من حرقى اذوب صبابة

لولا تجود علىّ فيض دموعى

ووعدتمونى فى الخيال بزورة

فتضاعفت حرقى وزاد ولوعى

ان كان ذنبى صدّنى عن وصلكم

فاليكموا فقرى اعز شفيعى

ماضى القطيعة لا يعاد وما جرى

كافٍ وحسبى ذلتى وخضوعى

قال الشيخ تاه لقد رثيت لمصابه، وبكيت لاوصابه،
ولا شيء انكى من الاغتراب، بعد الاقتراب، ولا امر
من الحجاب، بعد مشاهدة الاحباب،

~~~~~~

اشارة الدرة

قال فبينما هو كلما نظر الى ريشه نظره ، تذكر
تلك الحضره ، جـدد للحسـره ، وكلما نظر الى ساقه
صاح وصعد الزفره ، اذ رايت الى جانبه دُرّه ، وقد
كسيت ثياب للحضره ، كانها للناظرين حضره ،
فصاحت بفصاحتها ايها الطاووس ، الى كم هذا
العبوس ، انت فى الصورة عروس ، وفى المعنى كظلمة
الناووس ، اوقفك الراى المعكوس ، حتى اخرجك من
مكانك المانوس ، وما اخرجت من منزلتك الا لخيانتك
على الساكن ، وحركتك فى الامر الساكن ، فلو
فكرت فى السبب الذى اخرجت به ، والرجل الذى
طردت بسببه ، لاشغلك اصلاح شانك ، على التنزه فى
بستانك ، ويجب عليك كما جنيت على ادم فى تلك
الدار ، ان تشتغل هاهنا بالاعتذار ، وتشاركه فى
الاستغفار ، وتزاحمه فى خلوات الاذكار ، وتعترف
بذنبك بعد الانكار ، لعلك ان تزور معه اذا زار ، لانه

لا بد ان يعود ، وتعود له ايام السعود ، فان ادم
لما اخرج الى مزرعة الوجود ، قيل له ازرع اليوم ما
هو فى غد محصود ، وما عسى ان نفعه عليك يعود ،
فاذا انتهى زرعك ونمى فرعك تعد الى مقامك
المحمود ، على رغم العدو والحسود ، ومن عمل عملك
فهو مسعود ، ومن حذا حذوك فهو موعود بدار الخلود،
الا ترانى لما علت همتى، وسمت عزمتى ، كيف غلت
قيمتى ، فلم ارض لنفسى ، ما يرتضيه ابناء جنسى ،
لكنى نظرت الى الوجود ، وما فيه موجود ، فرايت
ادم وبنيه من دون الكل هو المقصود ، خلق الله
الكائنات من اجلكم وخلقكم من اجله ، فوصل حبلكم
بحبله ، وفعل معكم ما هو من اهله ، فلذلك زاحمتكم
فى كلامكم ، وشاركتكم فى طعامكم، فاتشبه بكم وان لم اكن
منكم ، واتخلق بكم ، واخاطبكم ، ولا ارغب عنكم ، فعلت
قيمتى، اذ علت همتى ، فاحلونى محل النديم ، والى بينى
وبينكم السميع العليم ، فاذكر كما يذكرون ، واشكر
كما يشكرون ، فلعلكم عند اللقا يذكرونى ، واذا
ذكرت يشكرونى ، فاكون فى الدنيا من خدامكم ،
وفى الاخرة تحت اقدامكم ،

شعر

اختبر حالى تجــدنى
من اجل الناس مخبــر
انا قد احببت قوما
شرفوا معنى ومنظــر
كبروا قدرا وذكرا
فهُمُ ازكى واطهــر
هكذا قد قال حقــا
سيد الناس وبــشّــر
كل من بهوى حبيبا
فمع المحبوب يحشــر

قال فلما سام نفسه بهذا السوم ، وجلس بمجالس
صدر القوم ، قلت ما رايت كليوم ، البهائم فى اليقظة
وانا فى النوم ، فمالى لا ازحم على ابواب ذى المراحم ،
لعل يوهب مرحوم لراحم ، و يقال مرحبا بالقادم ،
ها قد وهبنا الجناية للنادم ،

———

اشارة الخفاش

قال فنادانى الخفاش، وهو فى ارتعاد وارتعاش،
اياك والزحام، فلقد حام حول الحمى حام، وما ادنى
القسام الا لسام،

شعر

فما المنا يدنو بسمر القنـا
ولا العلى يعـطى بحد الحسـام

ولكن عليك باوقات، الخلوات، والقيام فى الليالى
المظلمات، الا ترانى اذا طلعت الشمس دخـلت الى
وكرى، واذا غابت صفت لى خلوة فكرى، فانا فى
النهار لا ازور ولا ازار، محجوب عن الابصار، محبوب
الى ذوى الاستبصار، فاذا جن ليلى، جررت ذيلى،
وجعلت الليل معاشى، وفيه انتعاشى، لان فيه يفتح
الباب، ويرفع الحجاب، ويخلو الحب بالاحباب،

وتغفل عين الرقبا، وتفيض اجفان الحبيب والغربا،
ويفتح للحبيب بابه، ويرفع حجابه، ويحامى احبابه،
وينادى احزابه، فترفع الوسائل، بالدمع السائل،
ويجاب السائل، بالطف المسائل، ويقال يا جبريل
ازم فلانا واقم فلانا، وقل لمن كتم حبنا حتى يصرح
اعلانا، وقل لمن هو ظمان، هذا الكاس ملان،
وقل لمن فى حبنا ولهان، ان الوصل قد آن،

شعر

لا يبعدنك عتبنا عن بابنــا
فالعهد باق والــوداد مــصان
فبهاؤنا وحسننا وبلـطفنـا
شاع للحديث وسارت الركبان
واذا ذللت لعزّنـا ذلّت لعزّ ـ
ـزتك الملوك وهابك السلطـان
يا ايها العشاق دونكم السبا
ق فهذه الشقـراء والمـيـدان

قال فقلت ايها الطائر الضعيف، صاحب الجسد
النحيف، ما لى اراك اذا طلعـت الشمس وقعت فى

العشاء، فلا تزال كذلك الى العشاء، فتعى بها يستغى
به الناس، وهذا خلاف القياس، فقـال يا ادمى
التكوين، لانى فى مقام التلوين، وما بلغت الى مقام
التمكين، لان المتلون لخائف، يدهش عند تشعشع
شموس المعارف، والمتمكن العارف، من ثبت عند
مهود اسرار اللطائف، وانما عدم تمكينى، وسبب
تلوين، وضعف يقينى، لانى مخلوق، ناقص لحقوق،
فبالنهار استر نقصى باستتارى، وبالليل اناجى لحبيب
بانكسارى، فيجود بغناه على افتقارى، وبفضله على
احتقارى، فاول ما جبر به كسرى، ورحم به فقرى،
ان جعل الليل خلوتى، ومع احبابه حضرتى، واليه
لا الى سواه نظرتى، فاذا انقضت خلوة الليل غمضت
عينى بالنهار لئلا انظر الى الاغيار، ويحق لمن سهر
الليل ان ينام النهار، وقبيح على عين تمتعت برؤياه،
ان تنظر الى سواه،

شعر

قبيح على قلب يذوب صبابة
وتـنـظـر عيناه لحسن سواهُ

ايجمل ان تهوى هواه وتـــدعى

سواه وما فى الكون يعشق الّا هو

اذا كان من تهواه فى الحسن واحدا

فكن واحدا فى الحب ان كنت تهواه

~~~~~~~

اشارة الديك

قال فقلت ناس لقد فاز اهل الخلوات ، وامتاز اهل
الصلوات ، ومنع من الجوار اهل الغفلات ، فعند ذلك
نادى الديك ، كم اناديك ، وانت فى تعاميك
وتغاشيك ، جعلت الاذان لى وظيفه ، اوقظ به من كان
نائمًا كالجيفه ، وابشر الذين يدعون ربهم تضرعا
وخيفة ، وقّ اشارة لطيفه ، اصفـق بجناحى بشـرا
للقيام ، واعلن بالصباح تـنبيها للنيام ، فتصفيق
لجناح ، بشرى بالنجاح ، وترديد الصياح ، دعـاء
للفلاح ، وان كان الخفاش قد جُعل الليل له وظيفه ،
فهو طول النهار نائم كالجيفه ، مستتر عن اعين الناس
خيفه ، وانا الذى لا اخلّ بوظيفتى ليلا ولا نهارا ،
ولا اغفل عن وردى سِرّا ولا اجهارا ، قسمت وظائف
الطاعات ، على جميع الساعات ، فما تمرّ ساعه ، الا
ولى فيها وظيفة طاعه ، فبى تعـرف المواقيت ، ولا
تغلو قهتى ولو اشتريت بالبواقيت ، فهذا حالى ،

مع قيامى على عيالى ، واشفاقى على اطفالى ، فـانـا
بـين الدجاج ، اقنع بالاجاج ، ولا اختص دونم بحبه ،
ولا اتجرع دونم بشربه ، وهـــذه حقيقة الصحبه ، ان
رايت حبة دعوتم اليها ، ودللتم عليها ، فمن هانى
الايثار ، اذا حصل القتار ، ثم انى طوع لاهل الدار ،
اصبر لهم على سوء الجوار ، يذبحون افراخى ، وانا لهم
كالخل المواخى ، وينتهبون اتباعى ، وانا فى نفعهم
ساعى ، فهذه شيمة اوصافى ، وبجية انصافى ، والله لى كافى ،

شعر

بـذكر الله يـدفع كل خوف
ويدنو الخير ممن يرتجـيــه
ولكن اين من يصفى ويدرى
معانى ما اقول ومن يعـيـه

~~~~~~

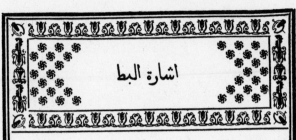

اشارة البط

قال فنادى البط، وهو فى الما ينغط، وقال يا من
بدنّ هيته انحط، لا انت مع الطير فترقى، ولا تسلم
من الضير فتبقى، فانت كالميت لا ارضا قطع، ولا
لزومك فى مكان واحد ينفع، سقوط نفسك القاك
على المزابل، ووقوفك عند الطل يجبك عن الوابل،
وما ربح فى المتاجر من لم يقطع المراحل، ولا يظفر
بالجواهر من هو واقف بالساحل، فلو ثبت تمكينك،
وقوى يقينك، لطرت فى الهوا، ومشيت على الما،
الم ترذ كيف ملكت هواى، فملكت عالمى الما
والهواء، فانا فى البر سائح، وفى البحر سابح، وفى
الهوا سارح، وقد جعلت البحر مركز عزى، ومعدن
كنزى، فاغوص فى صفاء تلألئه، فاجتلى جواهره
ولآلئه، واطلع فيه على حكمه ومعانيه، ولا يعرف
ذلك الا من يعانيه، فمن وقف على ساحله لم يظفر الا
بزبده واجاجه، ومن لم يحذر من دواخله ولجاجه، غرق

في متلاطم لججه وامواجه، فالسعيد من ركب قارب قرباته، ورفع قلوع تضرعاته، متعرضا لنسمات نجاته، مادّا لبان رجائه بجذباته، ثم قطع كثائف ظلماته، فوصل الى مجمع بحرّي ذاته وصفاته، فهنالك يقع على عين حياته، فيبرد من عذبه وفراته،

شعر

يا طالبا للمعالى
مهر المعالى غالى
قدّم فأول نقد
معجّل الآجالى
ما استعذب الموت الا
من ذاق ذوق الرجالى
حماه دون الوصال
حماه حد النصالى
كذا القصور العوالى
حُفّت بسمر العوالى
والشهد دون جناه
لذع كمرّ النبالى

قـد طاف حـول حمـاه

ذووا الجـدود الـعـوالى

وصـابـروا فى هــواه

عليه مــرّ النـكـالى

صامـوا وبالذكر قامـوا

فى مظلمـات الليـالى

فالروح بالشوق تـفـنى

والجـسم بالسـقم بالى

قـد صادف الحب مـنـهم

له قـلـوبـا خـوالى

ان كنت بطال فآثرك

مـنـازل الابـطـالى

~~~~~~

اشارة النحل

قال فنادت النحله ، يا لها من نخـله ، مـا جـ فى
روايتها رحله ، فالعارف من ظهر معنـاه ، قبل
دعواه ، وعلم صفا سزه من نجواه ، ومَنْ محى حقيقة
دعواه ، ثبتت حقيقة معناه ، فلا نقل قولا يبطله
فعلك ، ولا تربِّ فرعا بنـقضه اصلك ، واعـلم ان
بصفاء المـشارب يصفو الشارب ، وبـطيب المطاعم
يطيب الطاعم ، الا تراني لما طاب مطعمى وصفا
مشربى ، كيف رفعت رتبى ، وعلا منصبى ، وكمل
ادبى ، والا من انا حتى يوحى الى ، وينص بالذكر
على ، لولا انى اكلت للحلال ، ولزمت اشرف لحلال ،
حتى صرت كالحلال ، اسلك سبل ربى ذللا ، واشكر
من نعمه فصولا وجملا ، ابتنى المباح ، الذى ليس على
اكله من جناح ، فـاجعل فى لجبال بيوتى ، ومن
مباح الاثجار قوتى ، ابتـنى بيوتا يعجز كل صانع عن

تأسيسها، ويتخير اقليدس فى حل شكل تسديسها،
ثم اسقط على الزهر والثمر، فلا اكل ثمره، ولا
اهتم زهره، بل اتناول منها شىٌ على هيئتا الطل،
فاتغذى به قانعة وان قل، ثم اعود الى عشى، وقد
صفا كدر عيشى، فاشتغل فى وكرى بفكرى
وذكرى، واخلص لمولاى شكرى، ولا افتر عن الذكر،
ولا اغفل عن الشكر، فعلمت بالهام الوحى، وعملت
بالتوفيق الازلى، فانتج على وعملى، شمعى وعسلى،
فالشمع ثمرة العمل المقبول، والعسل ثمرة العلم المنقول،
فالشمع للضيا، والعسل للشفا، فاذا اتانى قاصد
يستضىء بضيائ، وان اتانى عليل يستشفى بشفائ،
فلا اذيقه حلاوة نفعى، حتى اجرعه مرارة لسعى، ولا
انيله شهدى، الا بعد مكابدة جهدى، فان اقتنصه
منى قهرا، احامى عنه جهرا، وادافع عنه بروحى،
واقول يا روح روحى، ثم اقول لمن جنانى، واستخرجنى
من جنانى، انت يا جانى، علىّ جانى، فان كنت
للرموز تعنى، فقد رمزت لك فى معانى، انك لا تصل
الى وصالى، حتى تصبر على حر نصالى،

شعر

اصبـر على مرّ هجرى

ان رمـت منى وصالا

واترك لاجـل هواى

من صـد جهلا وصالا

ومت اذا شئت تحـيى

واستعجـل الاجـالا

فسلك للحب صـعـب

يـقطّـع الاوصـالا

عذابه المـرّ عـذب

يخـفـف الاثـقـالا

ان كنت معنا تَبَعُنا

فـقد ضربت مثـالا

فان فهمتَ رموزى

اقـدم والا فـلا لا

~~~~~~~

اشارة الشمع

قال فسمع النخل استغاثة شمعه، فاصغى اليــه بسمعه، فاذا هو يحترق بالنار، ويبكى بادمع غزار، ويقول ايها النخل اما يكفيني، ان رميت منك ببيني، وفرق الدهر ما بينك وبيني، فانت فى الوجود ابى، وفى الايجاد سببى، فافردت عنـك بتحريقى، انا والعسل شقيقى، وهو اخى ورفيقى، فبينما نحن مجتمعون، وفى قرارنا ملتامون، اذ فرقت بيننا يد النار، ورمتنا ببعد الـدار، وشط ما بيننا المزار، فافردت عنه وافرد عنى، وبنت منه وبان منى، ثم سلطت علىّ النار، ولم اكن من اهل الاوزار، فكبدى تحترق، وجسدى تحت رق، فاهل الصحبة يتانسون باختراقى، واهل المعرفة يستضيئون بنور اشراقى، فانا فى اشراق واحراق، ودمع مهراق، قائم فى الخدمة على ساق، احمـل ضررى وضيرى، واحرق نفسى لاشرق على غيرى، فانا معذب بضميرى،

وغيرى متمتع بخيرى ، فكيف الام على اصفرارى ،
ودموعى للجوارى ، ثم تقصدنى الاوباش، من الفراش،
يريدون اطفائى ، واذهاب اضوائى ، فاحرقه مكافاة
لفعله، ولا يحيق المكر السّىء الا باهله ، فلو ملئت
الارض فراشا لكنت منهم فى امان ، كذلك لو ملئت
اوباشا لما اطفئوا نور الايمان ، يريدون ليطفئوا نور
الله بافواههم ويابى الرحمان ، وهذا رمز لمن تمعناه
بيان ،

شعر

قد اتى يا نـــور عينى

منك نور اى نـــورى

فهدای وضـــــلالى

بك يا كل سرورى

لم يطـق كل عذول

فيك يـرمينى بزورى

وكذا كل هـــواء

لم يطق اطفاء نورى

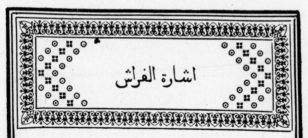

اشارة الفراش

قال فاستــغاثت القَراش ، وهو ملقى على الفِراش ،
يتلهب فى تلاشيه ، ويتقلب فى تغاشيه ، وقال يا
سه العجب ابذل نــفسى فى هواك ، ولا اعـدل الى
سواك ، وتسومنى سوم اعداك ، ليت شعرى من بفتكى
افتك ، ومن بقتلى اغراك ، اين لك مثلى عاشق
صادق، او صديق موافق، صبرت على احراقك، وقدمت
على الموت دون عشاقك ، فهل رايت حبيبا يعذبه
حبيبه ، او عليلا يسقيه طبيبه ، احبك فتعذبنى ،
واقرب منك فتفرقنى وتمزقنى ، يشتد شوق البك ،
فاهيم بالاذلال عليك ، اطلب منك الوصول فتنصول
علىّ وتحرق بالنار جلبابى ، فما اصاب احدا من
العشاق مصابى ، ولا عذب احد منهم بعذابى ، ولست
الى غيرك صابى ، وكان يكفينى ما بى ، لو سلمت من
توبيخى وعتابى ،

شعر

جئت اشكوا الى حبيبى ما بى

فرمانى منه بــسـوط عـــذابى

كفراش قد جا يطلب وصلا

فرماه حبيبه بـشـــهـــابى

وَهْوَ مُلْقًى لدى الحبيب حريقا

وغريقا فى لجة الاكــتـيابى

فى حسابى اذى وصلت ولــكن

سطوة للحب لم تكن فى حسابى

ذب غراما ولوعة واشتياقـا

هكذا شَرْعُ ســنة الاحبـابى

قال فلما ذكر الفراش مصابـــه ، وشكى تباريحه واوصابه ، رق له الشمع ممـــا اصابه ، وقال له ايها العاشق الصادق ، لا تـــعجل فانى لك مـــوافق ، انا مصاب بمصابك ، معذب كعذابك ، فاسمع قصة من اعجب القصص ، وارحم غصة من اوجع الغصص ، ليس العجب من محب يحترق ، وانما العجب من حبيــب يحرق ، هذه النار تحبنى ، وهى بانفـاسهـا تحرقنى

وتذيبنى ، وتطلب قربى ، وهى تذيب قلبى، تدعى
هواى ، وتستدعى لقاى ، فاذا نزلت بفنـاى ، فلا
بقاء لها الا بفَنائى ، وهذا لعمرى من اعجـب الاشيا ،
ان حبيبا يفنى ومحبا يبقى ، وعاشقا يسعد ومعشوقا
يشقى ، فنادت النار ايها المـعـذب باحـراقى ،
الداهش فى انوار اشراقى ، ان كان دخان احتراقى
الىّ راقى ، فهانا نازل فى العين اليك راقى ، فنشكوا
ما تلاقى ، وتفوز بساعة التلاقى ، فيا فوز من شرب
وانا الساقى ، ويا سعادة من فنا فىّ وانا الباقى ،

شعر

ولقد اقول لشمعة نادمتهـا
وسدول جنح الليل ذات جموح
انا من يحن الى الاحبـة قلبه
والى البكـا بدمعه المسفوح
قالت محـلت على فيا قلته
اسمع بيان حديثى المـشروح
ان كان اجملك الزمان بخطبه
فلقد فقدت انا شقيقـة روحى

افردت عن خل شهی طعمـه
حلو اللما عذب المذاق سرير
هل انت تندب من حکاه بریقه
او طعمه واراك فی التـبریر
واناله ها قد فـقـدت بعینه
او لیس بخل مدامـی بقیر
بالنار فرقت الحوادث بیننـا
وبها نذرت اعود احرق روحی

‏〜〜〜〜〜

اشارة الغراب

قال فبينما انا فى نشوة هذا العتاب، ولذة هذا
الشراب، اذ سمعت صوت غراب، ينعق بين الاحباب،
بتفريق الاتراب، وينوح نوح المصاب، ويبوح ما يجد
من اليم العذاب، وقد لبس من الحداد جلباب،
ورضى من بين العباد بتسويد الثياب، فقلت ايها
النادب لقد كدرت ما كان صافيا، ومررت ما كان
حلوا شافيا، فما لك لم تنزل فى البكور ساعيا، وعلى
الربوع ناعيا، والى البين داعيا، ان رايت شملا
مجتمعا انذرت بشتاته، وان شاهدت قصرا عاليا بشرت
بدروس عرصاته، فانتَ لدى للخليط المعاشر، اشام
من قاشر، وعند اللبيب الحاذر، الام من جـاذر،
فنادانى بلسان زجره الفصيح، واشار بعنوان حالـه
الصريح، وقال ويحك انت لا تفرق بين الحسن والقبيح،
وقد تساوى لديك العدو والنصيح، لا بالكناية تفهم
ولا بالتصريح، كان المواعظ فى اذنيك ريح، وكلام الواعظ

فى سمع هواك كالنبيج ، اما تذكر رحيلك من هذا الفج
الفسيج، الى ظلمة القبر وضيق الضريج، اما بلغك ما جرى
على ابيك ادم وهو ينادى على نفسه ويصيح ، اما تعتبر
بنوح نوح ، وهو يبكى وينوح، على دار ليس بها احد
مستريج ، اما رايت حال ابرهيم الخليل وهوفى نار الفرود
طريج، اما تقتدى بصبر الذبيح ، اما يكفيك ما تم على
داوود حتى بكى بقلبه القريح ، اما نهتدى بزهد المسيح ،
اى جمع لم ينفرق ، اى شمل لم يتفرق، اى صفو لم يتكدر،
اى حلو لم يتمرر ، اى امل لم يقطعه الاجل، اى
تدبير، لم يبطله التقدير، اى بشير، لم يعقبه نذير،
اى يسير، ما عاد عسير، اى حال ، ما حال ، اى
مقيم ما زال ، اى مال ، عن صاحبه ما مال ، اين ذووا
العمر الطويل ، اين ذووا المال الجزيل ،اين ذووا الوجه
الجميل ، اما قرضم الموت جيلا بعد جيل ، اما سوى فى
الثرى بين العبد الذليل ، والمولى الجليل ، اما هتف
بالمقتنع بدنياه قل متاع الدنيا قليل ، فكيف تلومنى
على نواحى ، وتستشيم بصباحى، فى مساى وصباحى، ولو
علمت ايها اللاحى ، بما فيه صلاحك وصلاحى ، لانتحت
بوشاحى، ووافقتنى فى سواد جناحى ، واجبتنى بالنواحى ،

من سائر النواحى ، لكن الهاك لهوك ، وحبك عجبك
وزهوك ، وها انا اعرف النازل ، بخراب المنازل ،
واحذر الآكل ، غصة الماكل ، وابشر الراحل ، بقرب
المراحل ، وصديقك من صدقك ، لا من صدّقك ، ومن
عذلك لا من عذرك ، ومن بصرك ، لا من نصرك ، ومن
وعظك ، فقد ايقظك ، ومن انذرك ، فقد حذرك ، ولقد
انذرتك بسوادى ، وحذرتك بترددادى ، واسمعتك ندا ى
فى النادى ، ولكن لا حياة لمن تنادى ،

شعر

انوح على ذهاب العمر منى
وحقى ان انوح وان انادى
واندب كلما عاينت ركبا
حدى بهمُ لوشك البين حادى
يعنفنى لجهسول اذا راى
وقد البست اثواب لحدادى
فقلت له اتعظ بلسان حالى
فانى قد نعتك باجتهادى
وها انا كالخطيب و ليس بدعا

على الخطبا اثواب السـوادى

الم ترنى اذا عاينت ربعـا

انادى بالنوى فى كل وادى

انوح على الطلول فلم يجبنى

بساحتها سوى خرس الجمادى

واكثر فى نواحيها نـواحى

من البين المفنت للفـوادى

تيقظ يا ثقيل السمع وافهـم

اشارة ما تشير به الغوادى

فما من شاهد فى الكـون الا

عليه من شهود الغيب بادى

فكم من رائحٍ فيهـا وغـادٍ

ينادى من دنّوٍ او بُعـادى

لقد اسمعت لو ناديـت حيـا

ولـكن لا حياة لمـن انـادى

ـــــــ

اشارة الهدهد

قال فلما كدر عليّ الغراب وقتى ، وحذرنى مقتى ،
انصرفت من حضرتى ، الى خلوة فكرتى ، فهتف بى
هاتف من سماء فطرتى ، ايها السامع منطق الطير ،
المتأسف على فوات الخير ، تأس لو صغت الضمائر ،
لنفذت البصائر ، واهتدى السائر ، وما ضل الحائر ،
ولو طابت الخواطر ، لبانت الامائر ، ولو شرحت السرائر ،
لظهرت البشائر ، ولو انشرحت الصدور ، لظهر لك النور
ولو ارتفعت الستور ، لانكشف المستور ، ولو طهرت
القلوب ، لظهرت سرائر الغيوب ، وشوهد المحبوب ،
ولو اعرضت عن الاسباب ، لفتح لك الباب ، ولو
خلعت ثياب الاعجاب ، لرفع لك الحجاب ، ولو غبت
عن عالم العيب ، لشاهدت عالم الغيب ، ولو قطعت
العلائق ، لانكشفت لك الحقائق ، ولو خالفت العاده ،
لما انقطعت عنك الماده ، ولو تجردت عن الاراده ، لوصلت
الى رتبة السياده ، ولو ملت عن هواك لمال بك اليه ،

ولو فارقت اباك لجمعك عليه ، ولو بعدت عنك
لوجدت الزلفى لديه، ولكنك مسجون فى سجن
طبعك ، مقيد بقيد مالوفك ، متشاغل بـشواغـل
نفسك ، متعلق بحبال خيال حسك ، قـد ازمنتك
برودة عزمك ، واحرقتك حرارة حرصك ، واثقلتك
تخمة بطرك ، واستعبتك عفوة رعونتك ، وبرضتك
وساوس شهوتك ، فانت بارد الهمه ، مقعد العزمه ،
جامد الفكره ، فاسد الفطنه ، كثير الحيره ، قد
انعكس ذوق فهمك ، فرايت الحسن قبيحا والـقبيـح
حسنا، فلو دخلت الى بيمارستان التقوى ، وعرضت
قارورة البلوى ، ورفعت قصة الشكوى ، الى طبيب يعلم
السر والنجوى ، ومددت اليه كف علتك ، ليجس نبط
علتك ، وينظر سحنتك ، فيعلم حقيقة محنتك ، فيسلمك
الى قيم مودب الشرع فيعقلك بعقال الخوف ، ويضربك
بسياط لعل وسوف ، ويروحك بمروحة الرجا ، ثم يحميك
فى حمى الحمايه ، ويكتب فى دستور علاجك ، باصلاح
مزاجك ، ويعبى لك اهليلج الالتجا ، وبنفسج الرجا ،
ومحمودة التوكل، وتمرهندى الهدايه ، وعناب العنايه ،
وسبستان السياسه ، واجاس الاخلاص ، وخيار شنبر

الاختيار، ويومى للجميع على ارض الرضى، ويدق فى
هاون الصبر، ويخل فى منخل الذل، ويصفى على
سكر الشكر، ويستعمل بعد السهر، فى خلوة السحر،
بحضرة الطبيب، وخلوة الحبيب، وغفلة الرقيب، لعل
يسكن الوحيب، ويبرد اللهيب، ويعود القلب
السليب، ويعتدل التركيب، وينفع مع يقظتك، فنسمع
هل من سائل فاستجيب، ويستنير بصر بصيرتك،
فتشاهد كل معنى غريب، وترى كل امر عجيب، الا
ترى الى الهدهد حين حسنت سيرته، وصفت سريرته،
كيف نفذت بصيرته، فتراه يشاهد بالنظر، ما
تجبه الارض عن سائر البشر، فيرى فى بطنها الماء
الثجاج، كما تراه انت فى الزجاج، ويقول بحة ذوقه،
وصدقه، هذا عذب فرأت وهذا ملح أجاج، ويقول
انا الذى اوتيت مع سخر للجهان، ما لم يؤته سليمان،
هو اعطى ملكا لا ينبغى لاحد من بعك، وانا اوتيت
علما، لا يعلمه هو ولا احد من جنك، كنت معه حيث
ما سرى، وجنّ به السرى، أدله على الماء من تحت
الثرى، فغبت عنه ساعه، فعدم الاستطاعه، فعوض
اتباعه واشياعه، وقال مالى لا ارى الهدهد ام كان

من الغائبين ، لاعذبنه عذابا شديدا او لاذبحنه او
لياتيننى بسلطان مبين ، والعجب انه افتقـدنى حـال
افتقاره الى ، ثم هددنى بسطوة اقتداره على ، فقال
لاعذبنه او لاذبحنه ، والقدر يقول لا واﷲ لاقربنه ،
او لاهدينه ، فلما جيت من سبا بسببه ، وقلت أحطت
بما لم تحط به ، فزاد ذلك فى غضبه ، وقال يا صغير
الجَرْم ، يا كبير الجَرْم ، ما كفى غيبتك عنى ، حتى
تدعى انك اعلم منى ، فقلت الامان ، يا سليمان ، انت
سالت ملكا لا ينبغى لاحد من بعدك ، وما سالت
علما لا يعلمه احد من بعدك ، قد جيتك من سبا بنبا
عظيم ، وفوق كل ذى علم عليم ، فقال ايها الهدهد من
مع له السلوك ، اوتمن على اسرار الملوك ، اذهب بكتابى
هذا فذهبت بكتابه ، وعملت بجوابه ، وقـربـنى الى
جنابه ، وجعلنى من احبابه ، وكتبنى من حَجّابه ،
بعد ان كنت من ورا حجابه ، ثم كسانى من ملابس
اكرامه تاجا ، وكنت الى ذلك محتاجا ، ثم نختت
حكاية ذبحى ، وتليت ايات مدحى ، فان كنت ممن
يقبل نصحى ، فحسن سيرتك ، واصف سريرتك ، وطيب
اخلاقك ، وراقب خلاقك ، وتادب باحسن الاداب ،

ولو انها من الدواب، فانه من لم ياخذ اشارته من
صرير الباب، وطنين الذباب، ونبـــح الـكـلاب،
وحشرات التراب، ويفهم ما يشير به مسير السحاب،
ولمع السراب، وضياء الضباب، فليس مــن ذوى
الالباب

شعر

اصبحت الطف من مر النسيم سرى
على الرياض يكاد الوهم يــؤلمنى
من كل معنى لطيف اجتلى قدحا
وكل ناطقة فى الكون تطربنى

ーーーーーー

اشارة الكلب

قال فبينما انا مستغرق فى لذة الخطاب، منصت للجواب، اذ نادانى كلب على الباب، يلقط من المزابل ما يسقط من اللباب، فقال يا من هو من ورا الحجاب، يا محجوبا عن المسبب بالاسباب، يا مسبلا ثياب الاعجاب، تادب بادابى، فان فعل الجميل دابى، وسس نفسك بسياستى، واسمع ما اقول لك من فراستى، وما عليك من خساستى، فانى ان كنت فى الصورة حقيرا، تجدنى فى المعنى فقيرا، لا ازال واقفا على ابواب سادتى، غير راغب فى سيادتى، فلا اتغير عن عادتى، ولا اقـطـع عنهم مادتى، اطرد فاعود، واضرب ولست بالحقود، وانا حافظ للودّ باقٍ على العهود، اقوم اذا كان الانام رقود، واصون والخوان ممدود، وليس لى مال معدود، ولا سماط ممدود، ولا رباط معهود، ولا مقام محمود، ان اعطيت شكرت، وان منعت صبرت، لا ارى فى الآفاق شاكيا، ولا على ما فات باكيا، ان مرضت فلا

اعاد ، وان مت فلا احمل على اعواد ، وان غبت فلا
يقال ليته عاد ، وان فقدت فـلا تبكينى الاولاد ،
وان سافرت فلا استهب الزاد ، لا مال لى يورث ولا
عقار فيهرت ، ان فقدت فـلا يبكى على ، وان
وجدت فلا بنظر الى، وانا مع ذلك احوم حول حمام ،
وادوم على وفام ، عاكف على مزابلهم ، قانع بطعم
دون وابلهم ، فان اعجبك خلالى فـنفسك بلذبالى ،
وتعلق بحبالى ، وان اردت وفاق ، فتخلق باخلاقى ،

شعر

وتعلم حفـظ المـودة مـنى
وتمسك الى العلا بحــبــالى
انا كلب حقير قدر ولكن
لى قلب خال من الادغــالى
احـفـظ للجار فى الجوار ودابى
ان احمى عليهم فى الليــالى
وتراني فى كل عسـر ويسر
صابرا شاكرا على كل حالى
لا يبالى علىّ ان مـت جوعا

اوسقتنى الايام مر الثكالى

لا يرانى الاله اشكو للخـــلـــق

اذ على الله فى الامور اتكالى

احمل الضيم فيه صونا لعرضى

وفـــرارىَ من مرذل السوالى

فحلالى على خساسة قـــدرى

فى المعالى يَفُتَن كل حلالى

أشارة الجمل

فقال الجمل ايها الراغب فى السلوك ، الى منازل الملوك ، ان كنت تعلمت من الكلب زهدا وفقرا ، فـتـعـلم منى جلدا وصبرا ، فان من توسد الفقر ، وجب عليه معانقة الصبر ، فان الـفـقـير الصابر ، معدود فى الاكابر ، ها انا احمل الاحمال الثـقـال ، واقطع المراحل الطوال ، واكابد الاهوال ، واصبر على مر النكال ، ولا يعترينى فى ذلك ملال ، ولا اصول صولة الارذال ، بل انقاد للطـفـل الصغير ، ولو شيت لاستصعبت على الامير الكبير ، فانا الذلول ، الذى للاثقال حمـول ، وفى الاحمال ذمـول ، ولست بالخائن ولا بالملول ، ولا بالصائل عند الوصول ، ولا بالمائل عن القـفـول ، اقطع فى الوحول ، ما تعجز عنه صناديد الفحول ، واصابر فى ظما الهواجر وفى الهاجر لا احول ، فاذا قضيت حق صاحبى ، وبلغت ماربى ، القيت

حبلى على غاربى ، وذهبت البوادى ، واكتسب من
المباح زادى ، وان سمعت صوت للحادى ، سلمت اليه
قيادى ، واوصلت فيه سهادى ، ومددت عنقى لبلوغ
مرادى ، فان ضللت فالدليـل هـادى ، وان زللت
اخذ بيدى من اليه انقيادى ، وان ظممت فذكرُ
للحبيب مائى وزادى ، فانا المخبر لكم ، باشارةٍ وتحمل
اثقالكم ، فلا ازال بين رحلة ومقام ، حتى اصل
الى ذلك المقام ،

شعر

يا سعد ان جئت لذاك المـقام
فانـشـد فوادا فى حماه اقـام
وان رات عيـنـاك ذاك اللوى
عرّض بذكر الواله المستـهـام
يا عيس ان لاحت لنا يـثـرب
فالسير من تـلك علينـا حرام
لما بدى وادى العقيق انـثـنـت
ترفل فى مشيــتــها كالنعام

يا صاحبي اجرى معى ادمــعــا

شوقا الى تجمل بـــدر الـــقمــام

وقل اذا مـا مــرت فى روضـه

يا ساكن لحى عليك الـــسـلام

~~~~~~

اشارة الفرس

فقال الفرس ايها الفقير الصابر الطالب سبل المآثر،
تعلم منى حسن الادب ، وصدق الطلب ، لبـــلـــوغ
الارب ، ها انا احمل مباهلى ، عـلى كاهلى ، فاجتهد
فى السير، وانطلق به كالطير، اهجم هجوم الليل ،
واقتحم اقتحام السيل، فان كان طالبا ادرك بى طلبه،
وبلغ بى اربه ، وان كـــان مطلوبا قطعت عن طالبه
سببه، وجعلت اسباب الردى عنه تجنبه ، فلا يدرك
منى الا الغبار، ولا يسمع عنى الا الاخبار، فان كان
لجمل هو الصابر الجرب ، فانا الشاكر المقرب، وان
كان هو المقتصد اللاحق ، فانا المجتهد السابق ،
فاذا كان يوم اللقا ، واوان المــلـتـقا ، قدمت اقدام
الواله ، وسبقت ضرب نباله ، وذاك منخـلـف لثقل
احماله ، معاق لتفتيش ما فى رحاله ، ورايـــت ثم
حقوقا لا يستوفيها الا كل موقّى ، وطريقا لا يقطعها
الا كل محقّى ، فلذلك شمرت عن ساق ، وتضمرت ليوم

السباق ، وقلت لمن اسكره الطيش فما افاق ، وغره
العيش الذى قد راق ، ما عندكم ينفد وما عند
الله باق ، فيما من هو عن المراد مــردود ، وفى الطراد
مطرود ، هلّا نظرت الى الوجود ، وفهمت المقصود ،
واقمت على نفسك الحــدود ، واوثقــت جوارحك
بالقيود ، وذكرت الاجل المحدود ، والنفَس المعدود ،
وخشيت اليوم الموعود ، ها انا لما اوثق سائس قيدى ،
امن قائدى كيدى ، فكم اكل سائتى من صيدى ،
وكم لى على مسابقى من ايدى ، اوثقـت بشكالى ،
كيلا اصول على اشكالى ، واخذت بعنانى ، كيلا
اذهب الى غير ما عنانى ، والجمت بلجامى ، لئلا يفسد
علىّ نظامى ، والزمت بخزامى ، خشية من غفلتى عن
قيامى ، ونعلت بالحديد اقدامى ، كيلا اكلّ عند إقدامى ،
فانا الموعود بالجاه ، المعدود لجاه ، المشدود للسلامه ،
المقصود بالكرامه ، قد اجرى علىّ المنعم انعامه ، فامضى
بالعناية الازلية فىّ احكامه ، بان الخيل معقود بنواصيها
الخير الى يوم القيامه ، خلقت من الريح ، والهمت
التقديس والتسبيح ، وما برح ظهرى عزا ، وبطنى كنزا ،
وصحبتى حرزا ، فكم ركضت فى ميدان وما ابديت عجزا ،

فكم كسيت من السباق ، ملابس اهل الشـقاق ، خزا ، وكم حززت اهل النفاق ، حزا ، فكم اخليت منهم الآفاق ، هل تحسّ منهم من احد او تسمع لــم ركزا ،

شعر

للحــق بسير ســابــق مضمّر
تــنال فوزا من مضيق المحشر
يا معشر العشاق سيروا جهرة
نحو النبى الـطــاهـر المطهر
فالسابقون هم الذين تمتعوا
بجمال منظـره البديع المسفر
فعساك تلحق بالرجال فانهم
نالوا وصالا حين وقــت العسر

فجاوبته تاه لقد حــويـــت من الخلال اجلها ، ومن الفعال اكملها ،

~~~~~~~

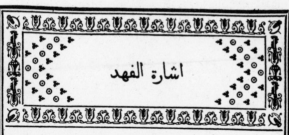

اشارة الفهد

قال فبينما انا فى هذا الجهد، اذ نادانى الفهد، تعلم منى الانفه، والاخلاق الصلفه، فانى فى الطلب لست كالفرس، ولا كالاسد اذا افترس، انا لعلو عزمتى، وسمو همتى، اراقب مطلوبى، واجالس محبوبى، واراوغ صيدى، بمراوغة كيدى، فان لم ادركه فى اول وثبه، غضبت على نفسى غضبة واى غضبه، فيترضانى اهلى فما ارضا، ويصيرون لى من التلطف ارضا، وما غضبى الا من التقصير، والساعد القصير، فيجب على من استوثب نفسه الى الكمال فنقصت، ودعاها الى المكارم فنكصت، ان يغضب عليها غضبة الانف، ثم يعود الى التوبة ويستانف، ولا يرضى لها بالغمة الدنيه، ولا بتخليط النيه، ثم ان فىّ لطافة معنا، لا يفهمها الا من كان معنا، وذلك انه ربما اعترانى من التخليط سهم ويغلب علىّ تحمى، ويثقلنى دمى ولحمى، فاخاف ان الطلب فادرك،

وإن ألقى فاقتنص فى المعرك ، فترانى أستوحش من
أبناء جنسى ، وأختفى فى خلوتى لإصلاح نفسى ، فأعالج
نفسى بنفسى، بترك المألوف وقطع العادة ، وأذيب
قلبى بالجوع الذى هو مخ العباده ، فاذا علت الهمه ،
وصحت للحبيه ، وصفا جسدى من العفونه ، ونفسى من
الرعونه، خرجت من عشى، وقد صفا كدر غشى، فحيث
شئت نصبت عرشى، وأيما انبسطت بسطت فرشى، وإن
كنت من رجالى، فجل فى مجالى، واعتصم بحبالى، واطمس
رسمك البالى ، ولا تبالى ،

شعر

انى رأيت الفهد فى وثباتـــه
ان لم ينل ما قد يروم فيهرد
وكذا النشاط فى الطريق مشقّة
لم يلقه الا اللبيب الجيّــــد

‏ــــــــــــ

اشارة دودة القز

فقالت دودة القز تاس ليست الـفـحـولية بالصور والهياكـل، ولا الرجولية بترك المشارب والماكـل، ولا الاثئار، ببذل النثار، انما الجود لمن جاد بموجوده، وآثر بحياته ووجوده، فان كانت خصال لخير معدوده، فاجلّها مع دوده، انا فى الدود كـدوده، ولاهل الود ودوده، انا المتوالدة من غير والد ولا مولوده، اوخذ فى البداية بزرا، كما ياخذ الـزارع بذرا، فاحضن فى جيوب النسا تارة وفى محور الرجال اخرى، فاذا تمّت ايام حملى، واذنت القدرة بجمع شملى، انفصل عن ذلك للحمل نسلى، وحصل من ذلك الـفصل وصلى، فانظر فى يوم ميـلاددى فلا ارى لى ابا ولا اما، ولا خالا ولا عما، فتكتنفنى ايدى الرجال والنساء، بالتربية فى الصباح والمساء، واحمى عن تخاليط الاغذية حائدا، ولا اطعم الا غـذاء واحدا، فاذا تمّ حولى، وبدت قوتى وحولى، بادرت الى شكر من انعم علىّ،

ومكافاة من احسن الىّ، فاشرع فى عمل ما يصلح
للانسان، قياما بمامور، هل جزاء الاحسـان الا
الاحسان، فابتدر من غير دعوى، ولا اظهار شكوى،
فانسج بالهام التـقدير، ما يـعجز عنه اهل التدبير،
فاسبل مـن لعـابى، مـا اشكر عليه بعد ذهابى،
واستخرج من صنعة صانعى ملابس، تـزين اللابس،
وتعمك العابس، فالملوك تفتخر بخزى، والسلاطين
تـتـنافس فى اردية قزى، فـى تجـدد الملاعب،
وتتجمل الكواعب، فانا اجمل المـطارف، وارفع
الزخارف، فاذا كافيت من احسن الىّ، واديت شكر
ما وجب له علىّ، جعلت بيتى المنسوج قبرى، وفى
طيّة نشرى، فاضيق علىّ حبسى، واهلك نفسى بنفسى،
وامضى الى رمسى، كمضىّ امسى، فانا الـذى اجود
بخيرى، وابالغ فى نفع غيرى، وانا المعذبة بضميرى،
ثم من نكد هذه الدار، المجبولة على الاكدار، انى
ابتليت بحريق النار، وحسد للجار، وقد اعتدى علىّ ظلما
وجار، وهو هذه العنكبوت، المخصوصة باوهن البيوت،
تجاورنى وتجاوزنى، وتقول لى نَسْجٌ ولكِ نسيج، وامرى
وامركِ مريج، ونحن فى الحرق سَوَى، ولا فخر لكِ علىّ

ولا سِوَى ، فقلت لها ويحكِ انتِ نحلِكِ شبكة الذباب،
ومجمع للتراب ، وانا نجمى زينة الكواكب الانراب ،
اما انتِ التى نطق بوهنكِ الكتاب فى الازل، وضرب
بضعفكِ المثل ، واين الكُحْل من الكَحَـل ، وايـن
البدر من النجم اذا افل ،

شعر

انى نجت القـز من لعـابى
سـر الاله المسلـك الوهاب
يا من اتى متشبها لفعالنا
هل تستطيع ملابس الاثواب
مـن لا يـكون نـافعا لغيره
فهو الذى فيها آدّعى كذاب

اشارة العنكبوت

فقالت العنكبوت، ان كان بيتى اوهن البيوت، وحبلى كما تزعمين مبتوت، فانّ فضلى عليكِ فى سجل الذكر مثبوت، اما انا فما لاحد علىّ منّه، ولا لامّ علىّ حنّه، من حين اول انسج لنفسى فى جميع الاوقات، فاسلم من منة الاباء وحنة الامهات، فاول ما اقصد زوايا البيت، وان كان خرابا فهو احسن ما اويت، فاقصد الزوايا، لما فيها من الخبايا، ولما فى سرها من النكت لخفايا، فالقى لعابى على حاقّاتها، حذرا من لخلطة وآفاتها، ثم افرد من طاقات غزلى خيطا دقيقا، منكسا فى الهواء رقيقا، فاتعلق به مسبلا يدى، ممسكا برجلى، فيظن الغرّ بتلك لحاله، اننى ميت لا محاله، فتمرّ الذبابة فاختطفها بحبائل كيدى، واودعها فى شبكة صيدى، وان كان لكِ الخيار، بما تنجيه من زخارف هذه الدار، فاين كنتِ عن ليلة الغار، وانا استر النبى المختار، واصدّ عنه الابصار، وامنع

عنه صناديد الكفار، وارد عنه ما لا يرده المهاجرون
والانصار، وكذلك لشيخ الوقار، الذى صحبه فى الـدار
والغار، على الشرف والغار، وانت ايها الغداره، التى
بزخرفها غراره، انما جعلت زينة للنساء الناقصات
العقول، ولهوا للصبيان الذين ليس لهم معقول، وقد
حرمت على الرجال الفحول، لان حسنك عن قريب
يحول، وما لك فى الحقيقة محصول، ولا الى الطريقة
وصول، فيا ويح مهجور منع الوصول، ويا حسرة محروم
حرم السؤل، ويا خسارة مطرود منع القبول،

شعر

بمقامير البيــوتِ	ايها المعجب فخـرا
لقيـام وقنـوتِ	انما الـدنـيا محـل
ضيقا بعد الفحوتِ	وغدّا تنـزل لحـدا
ناطقات فى الصموتِ	بين اقوام سكـوت
ومن العيش بـقوتِ	فارض فى الدنيا بثوب
مثل بيت العنكبوتِ	واتخذ بيتا ضعيفـا
بيت مثواك فـوتِ	ثم قل يا نفس هـذا

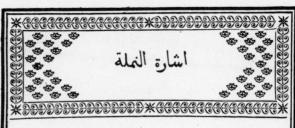

اشارة النملة

فقالت النَمله ، اذا ما رماك الدهر بهرما فتمّ له ، واذا رايت من تهيّا للمسير فسِرْ قبله ، ولا تكن فى تدبير عيشك ابله ، تعلم منى قوة الاستعداد ، وتحصيل الزاد، ليوم المعاد ، وانظر الى عزة عزمى ، وهِمّة حزمى ، وتامل كيف شدّت يد القدرة للخدمة وسطى ، واغتنى عن حلى وربطى ، فاول ما فتحت عينى من العدم ، رايتنى واقفة على القدم ، لاكون من جملة الخدم ، ثم كلفت بجمع المونه ، بتيسير المعونه ، ثم اعطيت قوة الشمّ من بعد الفراسخ ، ما لا يدركه العالم الراسخ ، فادبر ما اذخره من الحب لقوتى ، فى بيوتى ، فيلهمنى فالق الحب والنوى ، ان اقسم للحبة نصفين بالسوى ، فان كانت للحبة كزبره ، فلها حكمة مدبره ، وهو ان افلقها اربع فِلَق فانها اذا انفلقت نصفين نبتت ، وان قطعت اربعا انقطعت، وان خفت عليها فى الشتاء عفونة الارض ان تضرها ، اخرجتها فى يوم شامس فتجفّفه

التمس بحرها، فلا يزال ذلك دابى، وانت تظن انه
اردى بى، وتعتقده فىّ نقصا، وانهماكا على الدنيا
وحرصا، كلا واسه لو علمت حقيقة امرى، لاقت فى ذلك
عذرى، ولارتفع عندك قدرى، اعلم ان سه عزّ وجلّ
جنودا لا يعلمها الا هو، قال اسه تعالى وما يعلم جنود
ربك الا هو، فجيش النمل تحت الارض، لا يحصرون بطول
ولا عرض، ولا يحصى عددهم الا اسه، قائمون بطاعة اسه،
ولا يلون على غير اسه، متوكلون على اسه، ولا يلتفتون
الا الى اسه، فيقوم فيهن، من يريد ان يقوم عليهن،
فيستاذن لها تذللا، ليأذنوا لها تطولا، فاذا اذن
لم تخرج من غير خلاف، مبايعة على التلافى،
تنشد بلسان حالها، عند ارتحالها،

شعر

عليكم سلام اسه انى مـودّع
وعينى من الم التفرق تدمع
فان نحن عشنا يجمع اسه بيننا
وان نحن متنا فالقيمة تجمع

فنجتهد فى سيرها، وتحصيل خيرها، لنفع غيرها،

متعرضة للهلاك، ومصايد الاشراك، فاما ان تهلك
عطشا او جوعا، او تقع فى مفازة فلا تجد رجوعا، او
تختطفها ذبابه، او تطاها دابه، او يقتنصها طائر،
او يدوسها حيوان سائر، فمنا من يموت على الاخلاص،
ومنا من لم يقدر له على الخلاص، فنعود الى قوله تعالى
من المومنين رجال صدقوا ما عاهدوا الله عليه، فنلقى
ما فى ايديها بين ايديهن، فنقسمه بالسوية عليهن، من
غير خصوص، ولا حظ منقوص، فان كنت بالقبول
مخصوص، فانت النائب بالنصوص، وان كان جناح
عزمك عن العليا مقصوص، فانت صاحب الحظ
المنقوص،

اشارة العنقا

قال الشيخ قدس الله روحه وسره لكم البشاره، يا اهل الاشاره، ان فهمتم رمز هذه العباره، فانطقوا لضرب هذه الامثال المستعاره، والمعانى لمن اعنيت ولكن لابى لحديث فاسمعى يا جاره، قيل اجتمع الطيور وقالوا لا بد لنا من ملك نعترف له ونعرف به، فهلموا ننطلق فى طلبه، ونستمسك بسببه، ونعيش فى ظله، ونعتصم بحبله، وقد بلغنا ان بجزائر البحر ملكًا يقال له عنقا مغرب، قد نفذ حكمه فى المشرق والمغرب، فهلموا بنا اليه، متوكلين عليه، فقيل لهم ان البحر عميق، والطريق مضيق، والسبيل سحيق، وبين ايديكم جبال شاهقه، وبحار مغرقه، ونيران محرقه، ولا سبيل لكم الى الاتصال، ولو تقطعت الاوصال، فدون وصاله حد النصال، فاقعدن فى اوكاركن، فان العجز من شانكن، والملك غنى عنكن،

وان الله لغنى عن العالمين، اما سمعتم صائح القدر يصيح
ويحذّركم اللّه نفسه، قالوا صدقت ولكن منادى الطلب
ينادى ففرّوا الى اللّه، فطاروا باجنحة ويتفكرون فى خلق
السموات والارض، صابرين على ظما الهواجر، باشارة
ومن يخرج من بيته مهاجرا، فسلكن سبيلا عدلا، ان
اخذن ذات اليمين ارمتهن برودة الرجا، وان عدلن
ذات الشمال احرقتهن حرارة الخوف، فم بين سباق،
ولحاق ومحاق، وتلاش واحتراق، وتغاش واستغراق،
وبعد وافتراق، حتى وصل كل منهم الى جزيرة الملك وقد
سقط ريشه، وتنكدر عيشه، وتضاعف نحوله، وتزايد
ذبوله، فوصلوا اليه خماصا بعد ما كنّ بطانا، وجئنه
فرادا بعد ان فارقن اوطانا، فلما ان وصلوا الى جزيرة
الملك وجدوا فيها ما تشتهيه الانفس وتلذ الاعين،
فمن كان همته فى الماكول والمشروب، قيل لهم كلوا
واشربوا هنيا بما اسلفتم فى الايام الخاليه، ومن كان
همته فى الملبوس والنفائس، قيل لهم يلبسون من
سندس واستبرق متقابلين، ومن كان همته فى العرائس،
قيل لهم وزوجناهم بحور عين، واما اهل الحقيقة قالوا
سبحان اللّه اذا كان اشتغالنا ثم بماكول ومشروب،

وهاهنا بماكول ومشروب، فتى يتفرع الحب للمحبوب،
ومتى ينال الطالب شرف المطلوب، فالدون كل الدون،
من رضى لنفسه بصفقة المغبون، ثم قالوا نحن لا نريد الا
الملك الذى خرجنا من اجله على الحاجر، وقطعنا
اليه كل حاجر، وصبرنا على ظما الهواجر، حيث
قال ومن يخرج من بيته مهاجر، ثم لا نشتغل بالملابس
والمفاخر، فوالذى لا اله الا هو، لا نريد الا هو، ثم
قال لهم الملك وبحكم لاى شى جئتم، وباى شى اتيتم،
قالوا اتيناك بذلة العبيد، وانك لتعلم ما نريد، فقال
لهم ارجعوا من حيث جئتم، فانا الملك شئتم او ابيتم،
وان الله لغنى عنكم، قالوا سيدى انت الغنى ونحن
الفقرا، وانت العزيز ونحن الاذله، وانت القوى ونحن
الضعفا، فباى قوة نرجع وقد ذهب قوانا، ونحل
عرانا، واضمحل وجودنا مما اعترانا، فقال لهم الملك
وعزتى وجلالى اذا صح افتقاركم، وثبت انكساركم،
فعلى انجباركم، انطلقوا فداووا العليل، فى ظلى الظليل،
وقيلوا فى خير مقيل، فمن غلبت عليه برودة الرجاء،
فليشرب من كاس كان مزاجها زنجبيلا، ومن استولت
عليه حرارة الشوق، فليتناول من كاس كان مزاجها

كافورا ، وقولوا للعاشق الذى سلك سبيلا ، أشرب
من عين تسمى سلسبيلا ، فاذا صحت للحميه ، وتمت
الفنيه ، فقدّموا العليل الى طبيبه ، وقربوا الصعب الى
حبيبه ، فلقّام نضرة وسرورا ، فسقاهم ربهم شرابا
طهورا ، فسكروا حين شربوا ، ثم غنى لهم فطربوا ،
ثم استـزيدوا فزادوا ، وسالوا فاستجيبـوا ، وطاروا
باجنحة الانس ، فى حضرة القدس، فمقطوا ليلتقطوا
حَب الصحبه ، نقيا من الكدر ، فى مقعد صدق عند
مليك مـقـتـدر، فحصّلوا حين وصلوا، فلما حضروا
نظروا ، فاذا الحجب قد رفعت، والاكواب قد
وضعت ، والاحباب قد جمعت ، وشاهدوا ما لا عين
رات ولا اذن سمعت ،

شعر

يا قلبُ بُشراك ايام الرضا رجعت
وهذه الدار بالاحباب قد جمعــت
اما ترى نفحات الحى قد طلعــت
انفاسها وبروق القرب قد لمعــت

فعش هنيا بوصل غير مـنـفصل
مع من تحب وحجب الهجر قد رفعت
وانظر جمال الذى من اجل رويته
قلوب عشاقه فى حبه انصدعت

تـــــم
كتاب كشف الاسرار
عن حكم الطيور
والازهار

٢ ٢
٢

فهرس ما تضمنه هذا الكتاب

اصلاح ما وقع فى طبع هذا الكتاب
من التصحيف والغلط

الورقة	السطر	الغلطة	الاصلاح
٢٥	١٣	بللوم	باللوم
٣٧	٧	بعطر	بعطرى
٤٨	٥	واوضى	واوضى
٥٨	٢	كانت	كان
٤٣	١٣	كليوم	كاليوم
٦٦	٧	تلوين	تلوينى
٨٢	٤	ما	بما
	١٠	قصر	قصرا
٨٨	٦	يقطنك	يقظتك
٩٢	٥	ينطر	ينظر

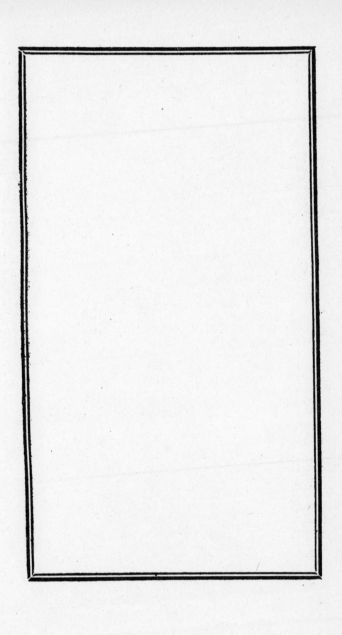